*Harlequin
Presents..*

VIOLET WINSPEAR

tawny sands

HARLEQUIN BOOKS
toronto-winnipeg

© Violet Winspear 1970

Original hard cover edition published in 1970
by Mills & Boon Limited

SBN 373-70539-5
Harlequin Presents edition published March 1974

Printed in Canada.

CHAPTER ONE

JANNA had been working for Mildred Noyes for about eight months and though she found the lady author rather demanding, it was better than the daily plunge into the typing pool of a city office.

Mildred travelled around in search of settings and plots, not to mention characters for her books, and Janna had no family to consider and at twenty was free to roam, and to be at the beck and call of her Majesty Mildred, as the young secretary dubbed her employer after only a few days of knowing her.

At the present time they were booked in at a hotel on the Côte d'Azur and its mimosa-splashed walls were a thing of glory, screening the indolent guests who were stretched out in lawn chairs enjoying the sunshine.

Janna had been sent out to the post office. A manuscript had to be sent off to Mildred's publisher, and Janna was there to perform such tasks, not to mention that of sitting up half the night before to finish typing the passionate intrigue set in Ruritania. The novelist never asked Janna's opinion of a story. Mildred took it for granted that every female who read her books found them too enthralling to put down until the last word. She called them an irresistible form of escape, and they seemed for a large number of women to supply a secret hunger for romantic thrills.

Janna was not a girl to believe in romantic dreams; perhaps too much of her life had been lacking in love. She had spent the early part of it in an orphanage, and the latter part in an office overlooking Piccadilly Circus, where she had worked amid the din of clattering typewriters, and girls who talked of nothing but pop idols, clothes, and boy-friends.

The opportunity to work for Mildred Noyes had come about through an advertisement in an employment agency Janna passed each day on her way to a ham sandwich and a coffee in a Wimpy Bar. She had paused, read it, considered the salary—which was slightly lower than her one at the office—and had been seduced by the words 'required to travel as companion and secretary'. That had clinched it. Janna had a deep longing to see beyond the traffic smog of London and she had gone to the Hilton Hotel to be interviewed—among several other girls and women, and two young men—and had been selected for several reasons Mildred had not been shy about mentioning.

Janna was alone in the world. She had no boy-friends to pine after. Her typing was speedy and accurate, her legs long and slender, and her disposition shone out of her English blue eyes. She was a nice girl. Mildred had seen it at once. Janna Smith was trained to obey, to be grateful, to fetch and carry, and not have ideas above her station. Nor was she glamorous enough to distract male attention from Mildred, who was partial to masculine flattery, though she never intended to marry again. The alimony from her ex-husband was too good to lose, and she enjoyed her freedom, and her fame as a popular novelist.

Having sent off the precious bundle of passion to London, Janna wandered into the hotel garden and sat down on some steps smothered in the velvety Côte d'Azur mimosa. Fluffy tiny balls of gold, not richly scented but giving off a sun-warmed smell of pollen and summer.

She let her fingers wander over the flowers and was enjoying these moments of relaxation when her attention was caught and held by two people talking together beneath some trees a few yards away from her. She knew herself to be hidden from the couple, a slight young figure in a pale lemon dress, lost in the mimosa, her fair hair in soft disorder about her sensitive face.

Her eyes took in with interest the silk, sari-like dress of the woman, whose companion was a man, conspicuously tall and so sun-tanned and supple that she didn't think he could be a luxury-loving Frenchman. Janna stared at him, taking in his iron-grey suit and the air of dominance with which he addressed the woman. The two seemed at odds about something, and the tall dark man was determined to have his own way. He reached for the woman's hand and several expensive-looking rings glittered on her fingers. He spoke decisively, and then quite clearly Janna heard him exclaim, *'Madonna mia!'* Which was very Spanish, followed by words quite beyond her understanding.

She began to feel guilty, though she couldn't follow the conversation, and was about to move away when the lovely woman broke into sudden tears. They gleamed in her large, lustrous eyes, and then fell down her cheeks.

'Raul . . . Raul . . .' She spoke the name clearly.

Looking stern, he bent his tall head and kissed her ringed hand. Then the tall Latin, with the air of an autocrat and the stamp of a man of means, swung on his heel and strode in Janna's direction. She chose that moment to spring to her feet, and without intention she found herself face to face with him. He stopped, as if startled by her, a flash almost of recognition in his eyes. Then it was gone and he was raking her from head to toe with brilliant dark eyes. 'Your pardon, *señorita*.' He passed on his way, confirming by his manner of address that he was Spanish, and leaving her with a vivid impression of him.

There was no need to try and commit his face to memory. As she lingered there in the mimosa she saw again his black and disturbing eyes, the finely sculptured nose with its tempered nostrils, the firm mouth and jaw. The face was a little cruel . . . a lot of it passionate with some suppressed emotion, such as would be present if such a man was not given the free rein that handsome, arrogant, supple creatures demanded.

He reminded her, somehow, of a panther in a cage.

But she mustn't linger here, thinking such nonsense about a total stranger. Mildred would rouse soon from her siesta and wish to dictate notes about the new opus. She had a fertile imagination and it seemed that the South of France had given her the idea for yet another of the romances her many fans clamoured for. She had said at luncheon in the Seascape Room that Janna must be prepared for a lot of work; that it was no use letting herself be beguiled by the sun and the sea.

She had said it rather smugly, as if Janna were her personal captive, chained to that cream and scarlet monster of a typewriter with its matching tape recorder. Mildred had the voice of an actress, and she loved dictating the thrilling scenes that had earned her the title of Empress of Emotion.

Actually she was one of the least emotional people Janna had ever met, who only warmed up and sparkled in the presence of a good-looking man. Had she noticed the tall Spaniard yet? He might—from his dashing looks—have stepped straight out of the pages of one of Mildred's novels.

In the week that followed Janna was kept so busy that she barely had time to catch her breath. She began to rise very early and to take a solitary stroll along the harbour while everyone still slept, including Mildred with her insatiable demands. When Janna wasn't at the typewriter or the post office, she was arranging her employer's hair, massaging her feet, or creaming the lines from the large face that had once been attractive, in a rather flamboyant fashion.

Mildred still looked striking when she was finally ready for an evening at the Casino, or on the yacht of a wealthy acquaintance, and being fond of imperial colours she thought Janna too terribly plain in her pale blue dress, or her velvet slip and white blouse.

At dinner the other evening Janna had been mistaken for a relative of Mildred's and invited to join a party on one of the yachts. 'This is my secretary!' Mildred had sharply dismissed Janna, and for the past few days the girl had been served her meals at an alcove table all alone, while Mildred lunched and dined with friends.

Not that Janna minded. It was peaceful to sit alone, where

she could gaze out of the window, or look around for the two attractive Latins and wonder if they were lovers.

It was strange they never appeared. Perhaps they ate in their suite because they wanted only to look and speak to each other. Or had they booked out of the hotel and returned to Spain?

Janna smiled to herself. She was becoming almost as curious about other people as Mildred, and each new face seemed to fit into the plot of a story. She was intrigued as to why that handsome Spaniard had made that lovely woman cry . . . love, she had heard, was not always a tender emotion, and he had looked shaken when Janna had popped out of the mimosa. His dark eyes had looked directly into hers, and she shivered in retrospect. He had looked every inch the son of a proud Iberian family, one accustomed to giving orders and having them obeyed. A man not to be denied once he had set his mind on something. A man who didn't care to be defied . . . by a woman.

Never before had anyone haunted Janna's thoughts as that dark stranger seemed to. While living and working in London she had gone out on few dates. She found young men of her own age rather too brash and obvious; all they seemed to want was to dance to loud music, and to kiss and cuddle in the back row at the cinema. Their gauche and tedious company had not inspired Janna to want more of it.

For so long an unloved orphan, Janna was a girl with a secret longing. If and when she fell in love, she wanted it to be with a real man, who said wonderful things to her, and made her feel cherished.

Early on Sunday morning, with a week's hard typing under her belt, Janna arose early and decided to stroll along the beach to where the sea was blue and creamy. Only a few fishermen were about as she made her way towards the shimmering water, where bronze-red nets were spread over the cobbled sea-wall. Small boats were beached there, giving off a salty tang of fish and sun-dried planking.

It was a gorgeous morning, and it felt so good to be young

9

and alive; so pleasant to walk alone and to feel the sudden crunch of sand under her sandals, and to hear only the calling of the birds as they flew over the blue water. Her name on Mildred's lips was becoming rather hard to take. The further away from England they travelled, the more demanding and bossy her employer became, as if she believed that she had bought a slave for ten pounds a week.

The only compensation was this place in the sun, the beauty of beach and sea, the splendour of mimosa and rustling palmettos. Janna wished herself a painter—if only of boats—and picking up stones she began to play ducks and drakes, skimming the white pebbles out on the rippling waves. She hadn't yet had time to buy a swimsuit; though she couldn't swim it would have been nice to splash about in the waves.

She saw that someone was taking advantage of the empty sea this early morning. A dark head bobbed out there in the blue, and a pair of tanned arms swung in rhythm as the swimmer began to make for the shore. It was a man, lean and strong in the water, with something so familiar about him that Janna stood transfixed, the stones falling from her fingers, a band of nerves tightening about her throat. Nearer, and then even nearer, until he began to tread water. A gasp escaped her. She broke out of her trance and fled away up the beach, her cheeks tingling with shock, and her heart pounding with excitement. So the Spaniard had not left the Côte d'Azur! He was still around. He liked to swim early, and quite obviously he hadn't expected a girl to be on the beach this morning.

She reached the shelter of a beached boat and stood there with her back to the sea, catching her breath. She had the other day likened him to a panther. Now she knew why! He was as lean, active, and as rippling with tight-coiled muscle as one of those superb jungle creatures. Nor had he the least sense of shame; upon noticing her, he had not retreated back into the cover of the waves but had continued towards the beach, bronzed from his throat to his heels, naked as a statue of Apollo in a pagan garden.

He must have left his towel and his clothes behind one of the rocks. He must also have been a quick dresser, for Janna was about to depart for the hotel when footsteps crunched the sand behind her and a voice spoke.

'So we meet again, *señorita*, to startle each other.'

She swung round, aware that colour had stormed into her cheeks at his approach and his remark, spoken in fault-less English with a certain emphasis on the sibilants.

'I ... I thought I had the beach to myself,' she managed to say breathlessly.

'I thought the same thing of myself.' A smile glimmered deep in his black eyes; he was fully aware that she had seen him clothed in nothing but his wet, bronzed skin. Clad now in a cashmere sweater and black corded slacks he retained his look of litheness ... and a certain danger.

'Do you swim, *señorita*?' With a lazy air, his black hair agleam from his swim, he took a cigarette case from a pocket of his slacks and flicked it open for her.

'No, I don't swim, or smoke, thank you.'

'Ah, an old-world girl in a very sophisticated land.' He didn't take his eyes from her face as he applied his lighter to his cigarette and let smoke trickle from his nostrils. Seen this close his face was even handsomer, yet not in a film star way, or in any way that was conceited or aware. It was a fine Latin face, but with nothing actually kind about it. His smile was not out to charm her. She felt instead that he mocked her a little for being a non-smoker, a girl who didn't swim, and who blushed to see a man as naked as Adam.

'You are a guest at the Splendide, is this not so? I have seen you with a stout woman who wears the most atrocious clothes. Somehow she does not look like your mother. An aunt, perhaps?'

He quirked a black eyebrow, and Janna couldn't help smiling at his description of Mildred, who thought herself attractive to good-looking men.

11

'Mrs. Noyes is my employer,' she explained. 'She is a famous novelist and I take her dictation and type her stories for her.'

'Ah, so.' He lifted his cigarette and drew on it lazily. 'She looks, this woman, as if she could make a lot of noise.'

His quip was too much for Janna and she had to laugh. Mildred would be so put out to hear this striking man making jokes about her, but Janna had known from the start that he was rather cruel. Had she not seen him make a woman cry?

'You seem so different from the lady of romance,' he drawled, revealing that he had more knowledge of Mildred than he had pretended. 'I could not imagine much fun for you in her employ. She looks very bombastic, and you are a slight young thing who might not be able to resist the weight of her self-importance.'

'Oh, I don't know.' Janna was confused by his reference to her figure, and a little annoyed. She had chosen of her own free will to work for Mildred, knowing she would have to put up with a certain amount of domineering, but she wasn't quite as down-trodden as this man implied. 'I enjoy the travelling part of the job. Two months ago we were in New York and that was very exciting.'

'You met some young Americans and had an enjoyable time, eh?'

'Well, not exactly. I had my work to do, but from the hotel window——'

'From behind the bars of your cage you watched the parade go by,' he cut in. 'You had to stay behind to make music on the typewriter while Mildred made her noise and danced all over the feet of the charming men of America.'

'She is my employer. She pays me to do the horse work,' Janna protested. 'I'm not a social companion.'

'You are not a horse, *señorita*, though you might be likened to a shy young filly who longs to kick up her heels.'

'How dare you!'

He laughed as he caught the blue flash of her eyes. 'Do

12

you ever manage to get away in the evenings, or are your escapes confined to the dawn hours?'

'It isn't any of your business, *señor*.'

'I am making it my business, *señorita*. I should like to take you out one evening, if the dragon in green will release you from your work to give me the pleasure of your company.'

'Oh.'

'Oh,' he mimicked, widening his own eyes. 'Have you no dress, no dancing shoes, no will to defy the dragon?'

'She doesn't lock me in.' Janna smiled nervously, and felt the dark fascination of his eyes, their assured dominance. 'I just can't understand why you should want my company. It's usually my employer who receives the invitations.'

'Your employer is hardly my type.' His teeth snapped whitely on the words.

'I don't think I'm your type, either.' Janna was innocent about worldly men, but she knew one thing—they became that way through knowing worldly women. 'Besides, there is your wife——'

'My—what, *señorita*?' His voice sank down, velvety and dangerous.

'The lovely dark-haired woman I've seen with you.'

'Rachael is not my wife.' He laughed, mocking Janna. 'She is my cousin, and only that by marriage. Now she is widowed.'

'Then the other day——?'

'Must I give you a family résumé before you will accept an invitation to dine?'

'I'm sorry to sound impertinent,' she blushed again, 'but I can't understand—I am not asked out by men such as yourself——'

'Then where have you been hiding, *señorita*?'

'You know it's true.' She spoke rather stormily, for it seemed to her that he could only want her company so he could use his wit upon her. 'Besides, I have no dress suit-

13

able for a night club.'

She was walking away from him when she felt the sudden warm crush of his hands upon her shoulders. He swung her to face him, and for a shocking moment she was close to his lithe black-clad body ... and it was like being close to a panther.

'Let go of me!'

'How charmingly naïve!'

'I happen to mean it.' She struggled, and in so doing found herself more perilously close to him than before. She glanced up wildly, straight into his eyes with their deep Spanish fire, their smouldering passions and intentions. She felt boneless, on the edge of some undreamed-of danger.

'The moth struggles and finds itself closer still to the flame,' he taunted.

'You have no right to—to behave like this!'

'Am I hurting you?'

'You are frightening me.'

'Why, has no man ever held you at his mercy before?'

'Y-you mock me as if you have the right to do so. As if I have no right to refuse your invitation. Has no woman ever refused you before?'

'Of course. I am not so vain as to imagine myself resistless, but it struck me that you are a girl who lives in the make-believe world created by Madam Noyes and that if you aren't careful life will pass you by and you will find yourself unable to escape from a woman who cares only about herself. Perhaps in holding you so you can't escape I prove my point?'

'Perhaps.' Her voice trembled. 'But how can you know so much about me? I haven't seen you since the other day. You never seem to dine at the hotel.'

'I stay at the hotel because it is in the vicinity of my cousin's villa. I like to dine with Rachael and her small sons. Sometimes I visit the Persian Room, or the Casino.'

'Where you have seen Mildred!'

'*En verdad.* And heard of the young girl she keeps

chained to a typewriter.'

'She hasn't mentioned you to me, *señor*.'

'I venture to suggest that Mildred Noyes regards you as a servant, not as a confidante.'

Janna bit her lip. Though the words were rather cruel, they were true. She was a typist and runabout, and so fearfully lonely at times that she hummed those orphanage songs to herself as she typed page after page of improbable romance in a setting all too wonderful to really exist.

'Do you deny the truth of what I say, Miss Smith?'

'So you even know my name.'

'Are you hinting that you would like to know mine?'

'I shouldn't mind knowing.'

'You are curious about me, eh?' His teeth gleamed white against his tawny skin. 'Now don't make a denial. Blue eyes are as easy to read as the heavens.'

'I should think the heavens more impenetrable than a coalmine.' She smiled and thought his eyes as dark as coal. 'Men have gone down to the depths.'

'Men are now flying to the stars, but that is beside the point.' He removed his hands from her shoulders, leaving their warmth behind, and gave her a brief, foreign bow. 'I am Raul Cesar de Romanos, at your service. In Morocco, where my home is, I have the name of Raul Cesar Bey. My grandmother is the Princess Yamila, of the desert province of El Amara.' His dark eyes held Janna's. 'Perhaps you were wise to feel somewhat afraid of me. In my veins runs the inclination to treat women as if they are pomegranates to be plucked from the wall of an enclosed court. Our villa in the desert is known as the House of the Pomegranate.'

From the beginning, from the first moment of looking at him, Janna had sensed that there was something unusual about the man. Now she knew why. The blood of a Moresque princess ran in his veins. He was proud, arrogant, and demanding because he was of the tawny desert.

'Raul ... Raul ...' that lovely woman had wept, and Janna had known from the start that he was a man who

15

turned away from the tears of women, but not from their kisses.

'You look a trifle awestruck,' he drawled. 'I assure you that the people of El Amara don't wipe their foreheads on my boots. I am—as we say in the desert—only a man, and all men are equal in the eyes of those who love them.'

Her blue eyes dwelt on his lean, handsome face and she wondered if he lived like a prince of the desert, and whether a cluster of pretty young women awaited eagerly his return to the House of the Pomegranate.

He smiled, as if reading her mind. 'Are you now satisfied that I am suitable to dine with? Or are you made doubtful, in case I carry you off to my harem?'

'Have you one——' And there she broke off in confusion, biting back the words, the colour reaching her temples where tendrils of her hair clustered like honey.

'In my country, Miss Smith, such a question is never asked of a man.' He looked wicked. 'It would be considered as impolite as asking an Englishman how much money he has in the bank.'

'I beg your pardon——'

'As a penance you will come out with me. Tell me, does Madam Noyes go to the Casino tomorrow evening?'

'Yes, always on a Friday. She calls it her lucky night.'

'Excellent. You will creep away tomorrow night without telling her you have a date, and we will meet here on the esplanade. My hired car is a Silver Cloud, so you will not mistake it.'

'But why do we meet in secret?' Janna asked, intrigued, not to say alarmed. What if he did mean to carry her off to some hideaway? It was not unheard of, but the girls involved were usually much more seductive than she could pretend to be. Mildred insisted that she was quite plain; the shy sort men never noticed.

'Your employer matches her name,' he said explicitly, 'and I don't wish half the Côte d'Azur to gossip about us.'

16

'Because I'm only a typist?' Janna's blue eyes held a flash of angry pain. 'I might be only that, but I have my pride and I can bear not having the honour of a Cinderella dance with a prince. It might make me dissatisfied, afterwards.'

'Little fool!' His dark eyes held anger for a burning moment. 'I ask you to meet me because it is important. I ask that it be in secret because I have a sound reason. I give you exactly two minutes to say yes or no to me.'

He stood there frowning, but Janna was determined not to be quailed by his arrogance, or his liking for his own way. She would not let his fascination blind her to the fact that he could also be cruel.

'Why is it important?' she asked.

'You are a woman and therefore inquisitive. If you want so much to know, then meet me tomorrow night. Come with me to the Persian Room and have your curiosity assuaged.'

'The Persian Room?' Her eyes filled with wonder. She had heard of the famous restaurant and been dazzled by tales of its splendour. Only the very wealthy could afford to dine there, and the man who invited her to go there with him was Raul Cesar Bey. Her heart turned over with excitement. How could she refuse? She could only give in and obey him.

'Very well,' she said, in a breathless voice, 'I'll meet you.'

'I shall be waiting.' He gave her his brief, foreign bow. 'And now return alone to the hotel. I don't doubt that Madam Noyes will be on the watch for you.'

'Goodbye——' Janna fled from him, pursued by a little demon that nipped at her for being so impetuous as to become involved with such a man. Mildred—if told—would be flabbergasted. When she recovered from her indignation at not being the one invited to dine with him, she would declare that he was out to seduce her innocent foolish secretary.

Janna was half afraid of that herself. He came from the desert, and he was handsome in a most dangerous way. She

17

gave a gasp as she ran blindly into a smother of mimosa ...
perhaps it would be wise, after all, to break her promise to
meet him?

CHAPTER TWO

JANNA told herself that it wouldn't break Don Raul's heart
if she broke their date ... and then the box arrived from a
famous dress shop on the smartest boulevard of the Côte
d'Azur. It came by messenger during Mildred's siesta and
was addressed plainly to Miss Janna Smith.

Feeling mystified, intrigued, and slightly alarmed, Janna
carried the large square box into her bedroom and quietly
turned the key in the lock of the door. She placed the box
on her bed and stood looking at it, rather as if she thought
it contained a snake.

Across the front of the box in gold script was the name
of the shop from which it came. Even Mildred didn't buy
her dresses there, not only because the prices were very
high, but because the style was beautiful, tasteful, and stun-
ning in a way that didn't hit you between the eyes.

In her twenty years Janna had received very few presents,
and this was either a present (surely not from Mildred) or a
mistake. She took a step nearer to the box, then another,
and suddenly with excited hands she was lifting the lid,
folding back the layers of soft tissue, and gasping at the
lovely contents. She drew out the dress, which rippled soft
and silky and was the colour of moonlight, with hazy,
subtle hints of blue. She turned to the mirror and held the
dress against her by the slender jewelled shoulder-straps,
and she could tell right away that it was her size.

Heart quickly beating, she sought in the dress box for a
card, and found it tucked away inside one of the silver
slippers that came with the dress. She took it from the envelope and read what was written upon it with bated breath.

Señorita Smith,

I am not exactly like the traditional Goody-Two-Shoes of the fables, but when Cinderella goes to the Persian Room she likes to look a princess. Please accept the enclosed, which I am assured will not fall into tatters at the stroke of midnight. Perhaps in your own country there is a convention which says a girl should not accept a pretty dress from a man, but in Morocco it gives us pleasure to just give.

I shall be waiting for you in the Pumpkin, at half-past eight tonight.

Till then,
Raul Cesar Bey

The card fell from Janna's nerveless fingers. She didn't know whether to bundle the dress back in the box and return it post-haste to the shop, or to be sensible and accept it. It was so lovely! Never in her life had she held such a dress in her hands, let alone been presented with one. But how did he, a bachelor, know her size? How could he know if he didn't possess an awful lot of knowledge about women!

She fingered the silver slippers, small and slim-fitting, and exactly right for her, and then she noticed another package lost among the tissue. It was a little velvet box, and her cheeks tingled with a shocked delight when she found inside a pair of lapis lazuli earrings in the shape of tiny hearts.

'He shouldn't! Oh, I can't accept these, or the dress——' But even as she whispered the words, she was clipping the blue gems to her earlobes and seeing how they matched her eyes. And her eyes were sparkling, half with fear, half with fascination. Would it matter so much if for once in her unexciting life she allowed an attractive man to dress her in silk and silver, and blue jewels? Who was there to care if he meant to seduce her? Only herself, of course. She would care if she allowed herself to be made love to by a man who regarded women as toys, prettily dressed up, feminine and soft, there to amuse him for a few hours.

And then her already bejangled nerves gave a sickening leap as a hand shook her door and Mildred called out sharply: 'Why have you locked yourself in? What are you doing?'

Janna stood petrified. Mildred mustn't see the dress or the slippers. She mustn't find out that a handsome Spaniard was pursuing her secretary. Being rather vulgar beneath her air of sophistication Mildred would at once assume the worst.

'I ... I'm coming,' Janna called back. 'I'm only ch-changing my dress.'

'Then be snappy,' said Mildred in a querulous voice. 'I want my neck massaged.'

'With pleasure,' Janna muttered. 'I'd like to wring it!'

As quietly as possible she hung up the dress and placed the silver slippers in a dark corner of the wardrobe. She then slid the box under the bed, where it was concealed by the long coverlet. She took a deep breath, smoothed her skirt, and unlocked her door. She stepped into the adjoining sitting-room and was immediately pinned by her employer's eyes.

'I hope you aren't keeping anything from me,' Mildred rapped out. 'You've been acting oddly just lately, almost as if you have a secret.'

'I assure you, Mrs. Noyes——'

'If it's a man, my girl——'

'I'd hardly be hiding him under my bed.' Janna was rattled, and speaking in a tone of voice that was not the deferential one required by her employer.

'Really!' exclaimed Mildred. 'You're becoming impertinent, Janna Smith, and I'll remind you that typists are ten a penny and only too eager to work for someone famous like myself. If you aren't careful, my girl, I shall dismiss you, and then what will you do, stranded on the Côte d'Azur with a few pounds in your pocket and no French to speak of?'

20

'Why, I'd get another job,' Janna rejoined, emboldened by the thought of Raul Cesar Bey's interest in her. She couldn't be totally lacking in personality if he wanted her company. 'There are plenty of hotels on the blue coast, catering for English and American tourists, and I could get a job as a receptionist.'

'You, my dear?' Mildred raised a sarcastic eyebrow. 'You haven't the chic or the self-assurance required in dealing with the wealthy and their demands. You would muff such a job in a day, if you managed to land one.'

'In which case I'm sure I could get a washing-up job in the kitchens.' Janna's eyes took fire and looked very blue, and in an instant Mildred was staring at the blue earrings Janna had forgotten to remove.

'Where did you get those?' she demanded. 'They look expensive.'

Janna at once looked guilty. 'Oh, I've had them a long time. They aren't really expensive, only good imitations.'

'They look fairly real to me.' Mildred's eyes were narrow as a cat's and a pale amber colour that made them look spiteful. 'Are you sure you haven't been up to something? After all, what do I know of your activities when I'm not here to keep an eye on you?'

'I should think the stack of work I get through each evening is a good enough answer,' Janna said stiffly. 'I'd hardly have time to rob the hotel guests, and you've said often enough that a man of the world wouldn't look at me. I presume that only a rich man could afford to give real jewels to a girl?'

'Your impertinence is intolerable today, Smith.' Mildred's face was flushed in a most unbecoming way, and her large body looked ungainly in a lace négligé. 'Go and take those glass baubles off your ears, and then come and massage my neck. It aches from bending over all that writing I have to do.'

From bending over the gaming tables was the real cause, thought Janna, as she retreated to her room to remove the earrings. She replaced them in the little velvet box and put it away in her bag. Her own cheeks were flushed, but quite becomingly. She would go out tonight, and she would wear the moonlight dress and enjoy herself for once!

Mildred said no more about their spat. She knew well enough that good typists like Janna were not so easily come by, not at the kind of wage she paid. Nor would they work so uncomplainingly. But all the time Janna massaged olive oil into her employer's rather thick neck, she was aware of the pale amber eyes upon her. Mildred was curious. She sensed that there was something different about Janna—a new look of assurance, a suppressed eagerness, usually associated with a man.

'You will get on with that new chapter tonight, won't you?' Mildred relaxed against the cushions of the daybed as a waitress appeared with a tray of tea and cakes she enjoyed after siesta each day.

'I rather wanted to see a film tonight,' Janna said bravely. 'I've worked late all the week, and my eyes feel like a rest.'

'They won't get it in a dark hole of a cinema,' Mildred snapped. 'You girls of today think life is a merry-go-round. You want to be treated like debutantes instead of wage-earners.'

'I think I do my share of work, Mrs. Noyes.'

'I pay you well—I mean, considering you stay here with me at an expensive hotel, and eat at my expense.'

'I know, but one evening off isn't much to ask.'

'You get the afternoons, while I'm resting. I can't have that typewriter clattering during siesta.'

'I'm usually running errands for you.'

'Really, my girl, you talk as if I'm a slavedriver!' Mildred sipped her tea and studied Janna over the rim of the cup. 'Have you arranged to meet some boy?'

Janna nearly dropped the bottle of olive oil all over the pile carpet. 'No, Mrs. Noyes.' And she was not being completely untruthful. No one in their right senses could regard Don Raul as a boy. He was the most masculine male Janna had ever encountered. Lean and vigorous from his heels to his brilliant dark eyes, and with something dangerous about him, something untamed.

'That chapter must be ready to be sent off by the morning post,' Mildred said sourly. 'You'd better start on it now, if you want to go out gallivanting. You know the *Romantic Woman* is serialising the story and they'll be expecting that new episode for the next issue of the magazine.'

'I'll do the typing in my bedroom.' Janna grabbed up the portable. 'So I shan't disturb you.'

It was a blessed relief to close the door on Mildred's annoyed face, and to settle down to the typing that had to be completed at least an hour before Janna was due to meet the Don. She wanted to soak in scented bubbles, and to take her time dressing. She could never hope to look beautiful, but she desired to look her best and the lovely dress would help . . . and if Mildred had left by then for the Casino, Janna had a dire plan to borrow the soft honey-furred stole that her employer rarely wore. She would take enormous care of it, and would be slipping it back into Mildred's wardrobe long before the novelist left the gaming tables and came home yawning to the hotel. The stole would look so much nicer than a coat thrown round her shoulders, and she had never dared before to borrow a thing belonging to Mildred, who had so many worldly possessions.

Janna's slender fingers flew over the keys of the typewriter, and as the minutes ticked by her sense of excitement increased. For one magical night she would live as the heroine lived in Mildred's romantic novel. She would dine at a super restaurant, in the company of a handsome Latin who knew the world as Janna could never know it; who was travelled and experienced, and had about him a certain air of mystery. The mystery that must be part of the desert, where he lived when he was not enjoying the sophistication of the Riviera.

It was twenty minutes to eight when Janna paper-clipped the finished chapter and sealed it in an envelope with a carbon copy. She covered the portable, stretched her aching arms, and glanced in the other room to see if Mildred had gone down to dinner. Everything was quiet. Janna was alone, and she lost no time running a bath and laying out her nylon underwear. She had a phial of favourite scent to wear, and though she didn't use a lot of make-up, her cream-powder and lipstick were attractively tinted, and a wisp of blue shadow across her eyelids was sufficient to enhance her eyes, which were her best feature and were darkly lashed in contrast to her general fairness. She had never known her parents, but someone had once suggested that she had Irish eyes.

Bathed, fragrant, and with a fast beating heart, she slipped into the silk dress and as its suppleness settled perfectly on her slim figure, and the jewelled straps gleamed against her pale skin, she caught her breath in wonderment. It was true, that saying about fine feathers making all the difference to a person. The texture of the dress, and the beautiful way it was made, created for Janna an illusion of real prettiness. The silvery colour with its hints of blue was exactly right for her.

Raul Cesar Bey was indeed a man who knew about women and what suited them. She dared not think about the price of the dress, with its hint of seduction in the jewelled straps and the baring of her slim young neck and shoulders. Her bosom was delicately curved under the silk, and her waist and hips were so slender as to be breakable. Her height was slightly raised by the fine heels of the silver slippers and the tiny blue hearts burned softly against the small lobes of her ears. Capping her head like so much mimosa was her short, well-brushed hair, and at her nape a little peak of gold was also innocently fetching.

She was all but ready. Now she had to brave herself to go into Mildred's bedroom where the honey-furred stole hung with other furs in the large wardrobe. Dared she take such a risk? Mildred would be furious if she ever found out. She might even accuse Janna of intent to steal, and all Janna

24

wanted was to enhance her dress rather than hide it with a coat. If only she had an evening wrap of her own to wear, but she had never thought to buy one. She had not anticipated an evening date with a man who obviously liked his partners to look pretty and glamorous.

She glanced at the travelling clock on her bedside table and saw that the time was creeping steadily towards her meeting with her escort. She must decide now . . . was it to be the fur stole, or her cream cloth coat?

'Mouse!' she exclaimed. 'What Her Majesty Mildred doesn't see she won't worry about. All you must worry about is getting back to the hotel in good time to replace the stole.'

Janna hastened across the sitting-room to the door of her employer's bedroom. She turned the handle, darted inside, and a few seconds later was adjusting the soft stole about her shoulders and fastening the big fur button. It felt delicious against her skin, and made her feel an expensively feminine bundle for Raul Cesar Bey to unwrap in the exotic Persian Room.

'Here goes, Janna.' She crossed her fingers. 'You're about to spend the evening with a dangerous man, so best beware. He'll turn your innocent head if you aren't terribly careful.'

There it stood in the parking area along the esplanade, a long gleaming Silver Cloud Rolls, with someone in a white jacket seated at the wheel in a wreath of cigarette smoke. Janna felt breathless, and she slowed her pace as she walked towards the car. As each step brought her nearer, she saw again the smooth black hair, the firm profile, the hint of autocracy in the way this grandson of a Princess flicked ash from the open window of the sleek car.

A most curious mixture of emotions assailed her. She wanted to turn and run away before he saw her, and yet like a piece of silver she was drawn towards the magnetism of the man. He made her afraid, and yet he fascinated her. She didn't dare to think of what he might ask of her; having dressed her in silk, he might take it for granted that she was his for the night.

Her knees seemed to tremble beneath her, her heart seemed to turn over, for in that moment he turned and looked directly at her, and he seemed to possess her with his long, darkly brilliant eyes. As she stood there the esplanade lights shimmered on her silvery dress and revealed her huge eyes in her triangular face, so lightly made up as to appear pale. She held the honey fur close against her throat, and there was about her an air of entreaty, as if she silently pleaded with him not to be too wicked.

He opened the door of the car and with a single lithe movement he was at Janna's side. 'Good evening, Miss Smith.' His eyes dwelt on her face. 'I wondered if at the last minute you would be afraid to meet me.'

'Good evening, *señor*.' She smiled nervously. 'As you can see, I plucked up the courage and came.'

'And you are wearing the dress. I'm pleased.' He said it like a sultan, and colour warmed her cheeks.

'It was rather wicked of you to send it, and rather greedy of me to wear it.'

'Greedy, Miss Smith?' He quirked a puzzled eyebrow.

'Yes. I was taught as an orphan child to suppress the desire for worldly things, and you tempt me with a dress you knew I'd be unable to resist.'

'So you like it?'

'I . . . I love it,' she had to admit.

'Then that is all you need worry about. No matter what your orphanage taught you, it isn't good for the spirit even if it's good for the soul to repress every desire for the good things put into this world for us to enjoy. Would there be moonlight if we were not meant to see it? Would there be sunlight if we were not meant to feel it?'

'Those things are universal possessions, *señor*.'

'Meaning that a girl from an orphanage is not supposed to want silk dresses?'

'Something like that. The Principal was hot on humility.'

'And having been taught humility you are guilty about feeling spoiled for once?'

'Yes—I suppose so.'

'Little fool. You amuse me, and you exasperate me,' he growled. 'Into the car with you—and don't crush yourself up in the corner like that! There is room enough for the two of us.'

Ample room, in that luxurious interior, with its springy upholstery, soft lighting, and carpet underfoot, and its aroma of good tobacco and well-groomed masculinity.

He started the smooth engine and they swept out on to the highway as if on wings. Plenty of traffic was about, coming and going along the wide road, splashing the night with long broad fingers of light. His attention was upon his driving for those first minutes, and Janna was free to study him.

He wore a crisp white dinner jacket over dark trousers tailored perfectly to his lean length of leg. His shirt front just hinted at a ruffle, and his tie was a narrow bow. In his lapel there was a small dark-red clove flower, and his cuff-links were gold with a tiny ruby in each one. On his left hand, on the small finger, he wore a crested gold ring, and his hands on the wheel were as well-kept, as lean and darkly strong as the rest of him.

Janna felt shy of him, here in the enclosed intimacy of the Silver Cloud. She was intensely aware of him as a man, and as a comparative stranger who in a matter of hours had induced her to accept an expensive gift from him, and to borrow a fur from her employer and so risk instant dismissal, or worse, if discovered by Mildred.

'Please relax,' he murmured, as if her tension communicated itself to him. 'My car is comfortable, the night is young, and I'm sure Cinderella enjoyed herself when she escaped from her chores for a few hours.'

'That is only a story, Don Raul. This is all too real, and I'm not sure I shouldn't ask you to drive me back to the hotel.'

'You could ask,' he drawled, 'but I would not comply with your request. My dear girl, you would not have met me in the first place, wearing the new dress, if you had not wanted to taste forbidden fruit for once.'

'I'm not sure I like the way you put it!'

He laughed. 'How easily alarmed is the little bird Mildred Noyes has caged for herself! I wager that the longer you are with that woman the more she will clip your wings, until you won't be able to fly away at all. Does not that prospect frighten you more than I do? I come from the desert, but the hawk is not quite so awful as the vulture, and your employer strikes me as one of those. Taking but never giving. Demanding, but never returning anything in respect of those demands. Arrogant without any kindness.'

'Are you kind, *señor*?' Janna had spoken before she realised what her words might imply . . . that she was aching for a little kindness, and that from him it would be more than welcome. 'I mean, you seem to like getting your own way . . . and I couldn't help but notice the other day that you said something to make the Doña Rachael cry.'

'The poor girl cries easily these days, and it takes only a name to bring the tears.'

Janna remembered that his cousin by marriage had been wearing grey and violet silk, colours associated with mourning, and she realised that Rachael's widowhood must be fairly recent. Dark eyes met Janna's as the car halted at some traffic signals. 'You never had a family, *señorita*, but I think you can imagine how it must feel to lose a loved one, especially someone who was young and with much to anticipate.'

'Yes, it must be sad for her, *señor*. And now she has to bear alone the upbringing of her children.'

'Ah, I hope in time that she will want to share her life with a man again . . . she is very beautiful.' He started the car, and Janna noticed that his hands were gripping the wheel, as if he himself were gripped by a strong emotion. 'Our table at the Persian Room is booked and I wonder if you have tasted champagne before tonight . . . the wine of freedom.'

As he spoke, Janna's hands clenched the honey fur of her borrowed finery. There was something about him that charmed her, held her captive when she knew it would be wiser to break free of his spell, before the wine and the soft lights added their enticements. She had never known a man like him before, and she knew herself vulnerable to a kindness, lonely for the attention of a real man, and responsive to the attraction of him.

'You are an intriguing creature, Janna Smith. You don't chatter or try to charm, and I begin to suspect that you have known very few men.'

'It would be a fairly safe assumption about a girl who isn't pretty or gay.'

'You think yourself plain and dull?'

'Without the fine feathers I am.'

'A little silken plumage helps any woman to look more attractive,' he agreed. 'But you are plain only in your own mind, and it no doubt suits Madame Noyes to encourage the idea. In truth, Janna, you have eyes of an unusual blue, and the soft hair of an infant. Ah, you give me an indignant look! You don't like it that you look so young and innocent?'

'I'd sooner look sophisticated.'

'Why, I wonder? You would still at heart be a soft and rather frightened young thing who has, I venture, never been kissed by a man.'

'Do you plan to remedy such a dismal state of affairs, Don Raul?' Her cheeks were scarlet, but she had to speak her piece. 'If you think I came out with you because I'm love-starved, then you're in for a surprise. I'm not panting to be kissed by you, because you happen to be handsome and rich!'

'I never thought you were,' he drawled. 'Nor do I have to seduce girls in order to satisfy my libido, *chica*. I am not some sheik of the desert, abducting a pale young thing with eyes like the blue hour. This is the Côte d'Azur, and we drive in my car to eat dinner at a restaurant—after which we will talk, and you will listen.'

'We will talk about what?' she asked.

'The time is not yet right for me to tell you.' As he spoke he drove the silver car into the parking area of the Persian Room, with its white dome and a Persian doorman, clad in the traditional kaftan and silk turban, to usher them into the softly carpeted foyer, with tubs of white oleanders and an arched entrance leading into the alcoved dining-room.

Janna was entranced by the jewel lights of the lamps, the tables set beside divans, and the strange rhythm of the hidden music. The aroma of good food hung on the air, mingling with that of roses entwining the marble columns of the dining alcoves. The diners seemed to talk in whispers, imparting an air of mystery and intimacy.

A waiter led them to a secluded table, lit by the little jewel-coloured lamps, and near an archway where a fountain played among flowers in the dimness.

The Persian Room was like an oriental palace, and Janna felt as if she had been wafted on a magic carpet into a realm of fantasy. The touch of strong fingers removing the fur stole from her shoulders did not dispel the feeling. Raul Cesar Bey added to it. Here in this exotic place he seemed more dangerously handsome, as if its atmosphere brought out the Arabian in him.

'Please sit down, Janna.'

She did so, and he sat beside her on the divan, and for a long moment he just looked at her, taking in her slim shoulders made seductive by the jewelled straps of the silky dress. She tensed as his dark eyes lingered on her throat, and the young curve of her bosom.

'It is really amazing,' he murmured. 'I can hardly believe my eyes.'

'Don Raul,' she smiled nervously, 'I haven't changed from a duckling to a swan with one wave of your cheque book.'

'No,' he shook his head, 'I was thinking of something else—but we will talk of that later, when we have sampled the wine and the food, and you are more relaxed in my company.'

She was puzzled, intrigued, and faintly afraid. She sensed that he was going to ask her for something, and she was afraid because with each passing moment he seemed to captivate her lonely, untried youthful heart.

She needed a glass of champagne, something to give her the courage to fight his fascination.

CHAPTER THREE

THE dinner enjoyed by Janna at the Persian Room was a memorable one, followed by plums flaming in a honeyed glaze of brandy liqueur. They were delicious, popped quickly between the lips, while the Persian music played and moths drifted in from the garden to hum around the table lamps.

'Now we will have coffee, eh?' He smiled at her youthful enjoyment of the plums. 'I think you like it here, the mystery and the music of the place. For me it's a little like being home again.'

'You sound homesick for the desert, Don Raul.' The sweetness of the plums and the tang of the brandy clung to her lips as she looked at him with a smile of interest in her eyes. 'Why do you stay on the Riviera when you are free to leave whenever you wish?'

'I came to visit Rachael, and I stayed a little longer than I meant to because six days ago I stumbled upon a girl in a tangle of mimosa.'

Janna's eyes widened, an azure blue in the soft lamplight. He referred to her, and her pulses gave a startled leap at the

31

implication that he had felt so attracted to her that he had stayed to make her acquaintance. And yet she couldn't quite believe him. The Côte d'Azur teemed with lovely sun-tanned blondes who had little else to do but enjoy themselves and amuse men such as Raul Cesar Bey.

'I'm sure you're teasing me.' She studied the nearby loggia with its fountain and flowers. 'I'm not the sort men like yourself take a lot of notice of.'

'What do you know about men like myself?' he mocked. 'I am not spinning you a line. I had planned to return to Morocco a week ago, then I saw you in the garden of the hotel and changed my mind.'

'But why?'

'You wouldn't believe me if I said I was at once intrigued by you?'

She shook her head. 'I'm not vain enough to believe anything so improbable. You've met too many women to be struck sideways by a nondescript typist.'

'You are more than that, Janna. You are intelligent, and you are direct. You let me know that your head is not so easily turned by a man, or this glamorous place and the champagne.'

'I'm not used to them, but all the same I'm not a fool.' She braved the half-brilliance of his eyes. 'Why did you bring me here, Don Raul? What do you want to say to me?'

'We will have our coffee in that fountain garden, and there I will tell you why I wished to know you.'

He beckoned the waiter and told him to bring coffee to them in the loggia, then he rose to his feet and led Janna beneath the fretted archway to a seat near the fountain. Water flowers floated in the marble basin, their petals like the pale skirts of tiny ballerinas. The tinkling of the fountain made a soothing music, yet Janna felt a tension that was not eased by the touch of a lean hand on hers, fingering the fine bones of her wrist.

'Your pulse is racing,' he said. 'You are frightened, yet you stay to listen to me. I am glad you have courage.'

'Is it going to take courage, what you intend to ask of me?'

'Yes,' he admitted. 'It will take nerve, if you agree to my proposition.'

She looked at him in the mysterious light of the loggia, trying to read his face and all the time acutely aware of his fingers on her wrist. He was touching the little charm on the bracelet of her wrist-chain.

'You are superstitious, Janna? I see you wear a little talisman.' He examined the tiny gold fish which she had bought for luck, out of her first month's earnings as an independent person. 'Has the charm succeeded in bringing you some good fortune?'

'I don't really know. When I landed my job with Mildred, I suppose I thought myself fortunate. I longed to travel.'

'Have you ever thought of seeing the desert—ah, before you answer me let us have our coffee. I find it conducive to clear thinking, and that we must have after the champagne.'

The waiter arranged the coffee cups on a small table and poured it hot from a silver pot. Then he left them alone . . . so very alone, in fact, that Janna wondered if Don Raul had paid for the exclusive use of the loggia this evening. She added sugar to her cup, took a sip of the delicious brew, and regarded her host with large, enquiring eyes.

'Only those of the orient know how to make wonderful coffee,' he said, with a sigh of relaxation. 'You must now give me your answer to my question . . . have you ever dreamed of seeing the limitless golden sands of the desert? The radiance of an Eastern sunset? The secretiveness of a walled courtyard and the jasmine growing there?'

There was a certain seduction to the words, painting for her a picture of sunlit sands, and the cool shadows of a jasmine court. There was in his eyes a smouldering look, as of a man who couldn't wait to return to his own surroundings . . . who implied that he meant to take her with him!

As he read the look in her eyes, he slowly smiled. 'Why do you look at me in such an alarmed way? Did I mention

33

my *harem*?'

'Don Raul, are you playing cat and mouse with me? Or are you serious when you ask me if I should like the desert?'

'I have never been more serious, *señorita.* Come, does the thought of going there excite you?'

'In what capacity, *señor*?' She looked at him frankly, with a tilt to her chin. 'As your secretary, perhaps?'

'No.' He shook his dark head and took a slim gold case from a pocket of his white dinner jacket. 'I recall that you don't smoke, but you will permit me?'

'Of course.'

He lit a *panatella,* and a small cloud of smoke drifted between them, teasing her nostrils with its tang of fine tobacco, mingling with the aroma of the coffee and the scent of the clustering flowers.

'The house where I live is situated on the edge of the desert and surrounded on one side by groves of oranges, peaches and the pomegranate. On the other side the desert flows away like a golden sea to the foot of the blue mountains and many miles separate the oasis of El Amara from the nearest town. Yet we live a full and active life at the oasis. There is always plenty to do in the groves of fruit, and always there is the desert to explore.'

He drew on his *panatella* and studied Janna through the smoke, his gaze at once lazy and yet intent on her face. 'One can live on its edge a lifetime and yet never reach the heart of it. It is sultry and temperamental as a tigress, fascinating as a secret doorway, veiled in stars when the sun burns out of the sky. It beckons like a temptress, and sometimes in anger it smothers the villa and the oasis in stifling waves of sand, blown on the winds of the sirocco. Then we hate it. Then we curse it, but when the wind dies down and the dawn unveils in blue and silver, we fall in love again with its magic, its enticement, its strange beauty.'

He flicked ash to the tiled floor, and crossed a long left leg over his right one, his shoulders at rest against the back of the seat he shared with Janna. He looked every inch a

34

man who controlled his life and his business with a firm, assured hand. It seemed as if nothing could ruffle him, and yet Janna sensed that he was worried and disturbed; that in her hands lay the remedy that would erase the frown between his black eyebrows.

'If I asked you to come to El Amara would you agree, or would you jump to your feet and run away in alarm from me?'

'I—I should want to know your reason for asking me.' Her heart raced and she felt slightly dizzy, as if the champagne still clung to her senses. 'You have said you don't need a secretary, and I can't imagine how else I could serve you——' And then she slowly flushed as he drew a finger down her bare left arm.

'You have silky skin, Miss Smith. Azure blue eyes, and an innocence about you that makes a man wonder. Perhaps I want you for myself, far away from the restrictions imposed upon you by your orphan years, and now by your taskmistress who looks as if she had never felt the love she writes about so avidly.'

Janna gave a tiny shiver, not because she believed any more that he was a seducer of young girls, but because his mention of Mildred made her loom even larger as a cloud over the days to come, which promised no more evenings such as this one. Soft lights, strange music, delicious food and wine, and the excitement of being with a man who was treated like a prince, and who looked like one.

'You're teasing me, of course,' she said, forcing herself to be sensible. 'I'd be foolish to believe that on a magic carpet you can whisk me off to the orient. If I believed you, I'd never be able to face another day as Mildred's typist.'

'You think I talk like this to make a joke on you?' His eyes sparkled dangerously. 'I am not in the habit of playing cat games with a little mouse. Mouse you are, if you leave here without listening to my story. Mouse you will remain, if you return to that woman because you are afraid to take a chance with me.'

35

'I'm not afraid,' she rejoined. 'Only of being made a fool of. I could agree to go with you to El Amara and then wake up tomorrow to find you had left without me.'

'You think I am insincere?' His voice sank down low and dangerous. 'Members of my family are not accustomed to having their honesty held in doubt. If you were not a girl——'

She made a little movement of retreat away from him, but her eyes were held by his, and he gripped her hand. She couldn't have run from him if he had put her hand to his lips and bitten it with his strong teeth.

'Life has taught you to expect very little from people, eh?' He quirked an eyebrow and studied the slimness of her hand in his, its paleness compared to his own bronzed skin. 'Not the hand of a pampered young thing with little to do but make herself pretty, but with the emerald ring upon it, it will fool the Princess.'

'What on earth are you talking about?' Janna thought she spoke aloud, but she really spoke in a shocked whisper. 'I— I have no emerald ring.'

'But you will have—if you agree to my proposal.'

'Proposal?' she gasped.

'Ah, I should have said proposition.' He smiled wickedly. 'Your alarm is hardly flattering, Miss Smith. Do I look and behave like a *roué*?'

'No—but you say such strange things, *señor*. Please, won't you tell me in plain words what you want of me?'

'I want you to pretend to be a girl called Joyosa.'

Janna stared at him, dumbfounded. Each thing he said seemed more outrageous and fantastic, and yet she couldn't protest. She saw from his face, from the glitter in his eyes, that he was now in deadly earnest. She was nailed on that dominant gaze, transfixed like a moth on a steel pin.

'From the moment I saw you,' he went on, 'I was intrigued by your likeness to the girl I speak of—Joyosa. The other day you saw a man who was rather in despair about something, and then he saw you and all at once his problem

36

was half solved. He saw a way to keep a woman happy.'

Janna stared at him, and thought at once of the lovely Latin in the sari silk. 'Who is Joyosa?' she asked, in almost a whisper.

'The young half-sister of Rachael—whom you mistook for my wife. I must explain that my family is a feudal one. As a boy I had to learn not only to gallop across the sands of the desert, but to be a keeper of the fruit groves, and later on a man of business, and also a medic for my people if a doctor should not be available in case of an accident. I had to learn the ways of the world as well as those of the desert. I had to be masterful, and yet submissive to the rules that govern the male heir of a family in a ruling position.'

He paused and the moment was filled with the sound of tiny frogs in the petals of the waterlilies. Janna gazed at the strong face and the dark peak of hair that gave him a raffish look. He had been taught to snap his fingers and have women run to him, and he expected the same obedience of her, a young, unworldly typist.

He quirked an eyebrow, as if he read her thoughts. 'Joyosa, when a small child, captured the fancy of my grandmother and was made her ward. She did not live at El Amara, but while a schoolgirl she came once or twice to visit Madrecita. Once at a village wedding her pony took fright at the noise and bolted. I galloped after Joyosa, caught hold of her pony's bridle and saved the girl from a nasty toss. Ever since the incident it has been assumed by everyone that I had captured myself a future bride in true desert style. Always the idea has intrigued the Princess, though she said nothing at the time. I have avoided an open discussion about the subject, but as soon as the girl had completed her education I was instructed to fetch her from her home with Rachael so that my grandmother could meet her again . . . and I think make a final decision about a marriage between us.'

Again he paused, as if to let each word sink into Janna's mind. And each word as it sank seemed to have a little dagger edge to it. He didn't speak of loving the girl, or of being loved by her. 'Regardless of your feelings?' she gasped.

'My grandmother is a Moorish princess, remember. Her own marriage was arranged for her and because it turned out happily she has decided to arrange mine.'

'But it's so unfair! On you and the girl.' Janna looked at him with sympathetic eyes. 'Has Joyosa taken fright and run away?'

'You could say so.' His eyes were sardonically amused. 'Rachael has no idea where she is, though it was learned from two of her school friends that she had become friendly with a young man in her last term. We have made extensive enquiries in the hope of finding her, but they were unsuccessful. She has vanished with her young man, somewhere in Paris, I suspect, and I am left with the task of returning to my grandmother to explain that her ward has run away. That she obviously dislikes me, and the idea of living at El Amara.'

'I'm sure you aren't afraid of your grandmother.' Janna smiled at the mere idea. 'Surely, in view of your own dislike of a forced marriage, you are relieved not to have to go through with it?'

'There is a complication . . . in fact there are two.'

'And that is why you need . . . my help?'

He looked steadily at Janna, with eyes that smouldered in the lantern light. 'My grandmother is elderly and frail. She clings to her fading strength in the hope of seeing that all is well with me and the future of El Amara. Needless to say I love her very much, though she is an autocratic old lady bent on having her own way to the end. If she had to learn that Joyosa has run off to live with another man, she would be incredibly shocked and angry.'

'You spoke of two complications, *señor*.'

He studied Janna with searching eyes. 'You have never known a family of your own, so perhaps you can't imagine how it feels to want to protect those whom you have always

38

known and loved. The Princess is frail in health but still active in mind, and extremely self-willed. She might, upon learning that Joyosa has taken wing, be angry enough with her family to cut off the generous allowance which Rachael and her two small sons depend upon.'

He dropped the stub of his cigar into an ashtray. 'I hope with your help, Janna, to convince the Princess that a man's marriage is his personal affair. Will you assist me?'

'I don't see how——'

'I do see how it can be done. Joyosa was little more than a schoolgirl when she was last at El Amara. Girls change as they grow up, though they retain blue eyes if they have them, and a fair colouring. I plan to pass you off as Joyosa. I want to protect Rachael, and I want to keep the Princess happy.'

A smile came into his eyes at the stunned way Janna looked at him. He shrugged slightly, as if he didn't expect her to understand family involvements—but she did. She guessed that the Princess was both generous and imperious and could snatch away her gifts if her will was crossed. Don Raul obviously adored her, but he knew what she was like and he was concerned for Rachael's welfare. The tears she had wept had not left him unmoved . . . they had led him to suggest a deception that would ensure her security!

Was it possible he was in love with Rachael . . . a lovely young widow with two small sons by another man? A woman the Princess would oppose as a bride for her grandson. He was to take over at El Amara when she died, and so the children born of his marriage must be her direct descendants. Her pride as matriarch demanded this of him.

Janna had been left out in the cold as far as family loyalties were concerned, but she had a heart, and she had compassion, and her imagination was vivid. She wasn't at a loss to understand the predicament in which Don Raul found himself . . . divided between his devotion to the Princess and his masculine response to the lovely widow.

'But I can't see how a deception would help.' The words

39

broke from Janna. 'Your grandmother wouldn't be deceived.'

'Won't you take a chance?' He leaned suddenly closer, and Janna was startled by his nearness, by the dark strength of him, the purpose and the attraction. A shocking thought winged through her mind, and her body . . . what would it be like to be kissed by him?

'Don't look afraid,' he taunted. 'I'm not going to force you into anything . . . though there are ways to persuade a girl. I could appeal to your romantic heart; kidnap and carry you off like the sheik you glimpse in my eyes . . . the one which no doubt sent Joyosa running away when she heard that I was on the way to the Côte d'Azur to take her to the desert.'

'Are you regretful about losing her, Don Raul?'

'Hardly regretful! The idea of an arranged marriage appals me, and I knew all along that Joyosa was only a pretty picture without any real dimension to her. A rather shallow and selfish girl who had never suffered, or been anything but pampered. Whereas——'

There he broke off, but in her mind Janna supplied the missing words. Rachael had suffered! She had lost her husband and been left to rear and educate her two sons. She was lovely, with the great lustrous eyes of a Madonna, said to be the ideal of Spanish men, and Don Raul was as much a Spaniard as he was a son of the sands.

'You speak of Joyosa as a pretty girl.' A tiny wry smile clung to Janna's lips. 'I don't know how you mean to pass me off in her place.'

'You are far too modest.' His eyes held a slightly wicked glint as they took in her slimness in the silvery dress, the blue gems in her ears, her pale neck and shoulders caressed by fingers of shadow. 'My plan sounds very wicked to you, I can see that, but all my grandmother is expecting is a fair and slender young thing. Joyosa's mother was English, which accounted for her fair colouring and her blue-grey eyes. Yes, eyes more shallow than yours, *señorita*, but it will

40

be assumed that the colour deepened as Joyosa grew into womanhood. Come, I am not asking you to actually marry me. I merely want you to come to El Amara, to stay a while, and then be jilted by me when the Princess sees for herself that we are not a loving couple.'

'But I couldn't possibly agree to such deception.' Janna looked at him with shocked eyes. 'I'd be too afraid, and I'd hate the idea of misleading your grandmother. You say it's for her sake, but I believe you're more concerned for Rachael. You are safeguarding her interests.'

'Quite so,' he agreed. 'But I shall also be protecting my grandmother from knowledge that would have an adverse effect on her frail health. You don't know her! How set in her ideas she is. How determined that the new mistress of El Amara shall be someone she has selected; whom she believes will make me an affectionate wife. Strange how easy it is to be taken in by a pair of large blue eyes. One is inclined to believe that only innocence and honesty shine in them and they hide no secrets.'

'If I were only innocent, *señor*, I might be led into this deception. But I do happen to be honest as well, and I couldn't help you to fabricate a lie which I am sure the Princess would soon rip to pieces. She wouldn't be the head of a business if she wasn't shrewd, and wise.'

'She used to be as sharp as a needle and amazingly active,' he said, a little sadly. 'I can remember her in the saddle of an Arab mare, riding around the groves on her inspection, and galloping at full tilt across the sands. But now she is frail. Her eyes look back upon memories, and her only dream of the future is to see me settled down as a family man—with Joyosa. But Joyosa ran away from me, and I never loved her.'

'I still think it would be wise to be frank with your grandmother,' Janna said, and then she gave a gasp as Don Raul caught her by the shoulders and pulled her close to him. He gazed down directly into her eyes and there was nothing of pleading in his look, only command and enticement.

'There are many things for you to enjoy at El Amara,' he said in a deep voice. 'You will be left to your leisure most of the time, and there will not be a Madam Noyes to demand your time and your attention. And there is one more thing —and it may have alarmed you more than all the rest—I I shall not be an ardent suitor. We present for the Princess the picture of a couple cooling off.' His gaze fell to her mouth, so innocently curved and unkissed. 'Is it my kisses you fear? Are you afraid I shall make demands upon you? Foolish one! I am not asking you to show me affection . . . I wish you to be cool towards me. To be the little ice-maiden. The Princess believes that a woman should be warm, responsive to a man's ardour, and when she sees the reverse in you, then she will not make a murmur of protest when I announce that I don't want to marry you.'

'I couldn't . . . I'm sorry, Don Raul, but I'm no actress.'

'It would not be acting,' he mocked, 'to play the ice-maiden with me. I feel you trembling now at my touch, and your eyes are tearful. You have only to be yourself and the Princess will realise that she has condemned me to an icicle.'

'Please . . . don't try and persuade me!'

'You will be well paid, Janna, and I shan't ask you to run errands and write my memoirs.'

She gave a reluctant laugh. 'You are a devil, Don Raul. You are asking me to go against all my principles, to set aside honesty and become your partner in a lie. No, I couldn't do it for a thousand pounds!'

'Think what two thousand could mean to you,' he coaxed. 'Escape from Mildred Noyes, and the holiday of a lifetime.'

'But why me?' Janna almost pleaded. 'The Côte d'Azur is teeming with girls.'

'You, child, because you resemble Joyosa. I noticed it from the moment I saw you. You have her slimness. The shape of your face is similar to hers, and the colour of your hair. You have a wondering way of looking at everything, just as she once had. I am sure she has now lost it, but you have it still and it will not be lost on my grandmother. It was such a look that beguiled her, led her to believe that Joyosa would grow up to make her devil of a grandson a refreshing and innocent bride.'

The irony in his voice made Janna think of Rachael, whom the Princess would hardly consider innocent and unworldly. And so he had to find a way to convince her that a mere girl was not for him. That youthful chatter and dewy kisses would bore him. He had to prove this to her, and he needed someone naïve like Janna Smith; she would be ideal for his purpose.

Janna shrank physically from such a plan. She forced herself out of the clasp of his hands and jumped hastily to her feet. 'I want to go home . . . please!'

'You call it home?' he mocked. 'Being chained in a hotel to a typewriter?'

'It's what I'm used to, Don Raul.'

'Better the devil you know, eh?' He rose lazily to his feet, but his eyes were unsmiling and he didn't speak again until they were in the Rolls and speeding smoothly towards the hotel. Janna was glad he was driving fast. They had talked for a long time and it was late.

'I am sorry my proposition does not appeal to you,' he said. 'I hoped you had a sense of adventure, and the wish to escape from the drudgery of typing silly stories in a hotel room. I can see you are a shy sort of girl, but I thought I detected a small flame of rebellion burning in you, somewhere. I must have been mistaken.'

'Yes, *señor*,' she agreed. 'You must have thought me more desperate than I really am.'

'You would have to be desperate before you agreed to help a man?'

'I'd help anyone in real trouble or need,' she said indignantly. 'You want to use me for your own ends.'

'And what are they, Miss Smith?'

'You know very well. You may not wish to hurt your grandmother, who believes she has your best interests at heart, but to deceive her would hurt even more. Why not tell her the truth?'

'The truth can sometimes be more cruel than a white lie.'

'You wanted me for your white lie, Don Raul, and I wouldn't make a very convincing one.'

'Perhaps not,' he drawled. 'Even at fifteen Joyosa liked to be flattered and admired. You seem afraid of men.'

'A born spinster, *señor*?'

'It would seem likely, *señorita*.' His smile was faintly cruel as he assisted her from the car, and then suddenly he pulled her into his arms, made a captive of her before she could protest.

The night was still around them, but for the pounding of her heart, and the chorus of cicadas in the grounds of the hotel. Shocked by his sudden embrace, she was helpless to resist as he pulled her into the shadow of the trees, deep into the velvety mimosa, so that the night scents of the garden added something primitive to the moment.

Never in her life before had Janna felt the demanding strength in a pair of male arms, holding her close in the darkness, imparting to her every nerve her inability to escape from them.

She looked up at him and saw the dark glitter of his eyes, and knew herself at the mercy of a man who had desert blood running hot in his veins. Women were to him like fillies to be tamed, and the devilish smile gleaming in his eyes told her that she was about to receive a sample of his taming. Her heart hammered . . . she felt the strength that could have broken her in twain . . . and then she heard him laugh very softly.

'Let go of me!' she gasped.

'You are trembling so much you would fall to the ground,' he mocked. 'No, before I release you I am going to teach you a little about men . . . and women.'

'No——'

'Yes, my little sprig of mimosa. Yes . . .' His lips came near, his breath stirred warm against her skin, his hands

44

crushed her silvery slightness close against him. 'The time has to come for every girl to be kissed, and the time has come for you.'

'I—I shall hate you——'

'What, hate a man you will probably never see again after tonight?'

CHAPTER FOUR

HE held her slender body in a grip of steel and bending her over his arm he crushed her lips with his, holding her for long moments, compelling her surrender, sending shock-waves all through her being as he moved his lips in fierce little kisses all over her face and throat, lingering against her earlobe, his hand slipping from beneath the stole to press the silk-clad curve of her waist.

She gasped, twisted her body in an effort to escape him, and was bruised against his hard strength.

'Little fool,' he laughed low in his throat. 'I could crush you and there wouldn't be a soul to care. No one cares about you, do you hear me? You are flotsam on the noisy stream of Mildred's life, and she will never be concerned for you; will never care if you are lonely or tired or in need of love. You will be a little nobody all your life . . . if you don't break free of her.'

'Y-you say these things to hurt me. You kiss me just to be cruel.' Again she tried to break away from him, but it was like being chained. She had never felt such lithe strength; nor had she ever met such ruthlessness. She felt he could break her in his hands and toss the pieces to the uncaring Mildred.

Then abruptly he let her go, and she staggered back against the bonnet of the long silver car. She stared at him, her eyes enormous and hurt in the pale triangle of her face, her lips red as crushed berries. The mink stole hung limp against her dress, her hair was ruffled against her temples.

Raul Cesar Bey regarded her in the manner of a sultan who had had his way and was now about to dismiss her.

'It has been an unusual evening,' he said, one hand straightening his tie, the dark-red clove lost from his lapel. 'I shall remember it when I am back in Morocco.'

'Why, Don Raul,' she gathered around her the remnants of her dignity and spoke with all the coolness she could muster, 'because for once a woman wouldn't bow to your wishes?'

'Yes, I shall remember that, among other things.' His gaze slipped over her. 'You are foolish to suppose you are worth only the crumbs from life's table. Think about it, Janna Smith. Even if you won't come with me to El Amara——'

'I can't.' The words broke from her. 'Not at any price.'

'Then so be it.' He spread his hands in a fatalistic gesture. 'As we say in the desert, what is written in the stars must be revealed in actions. I will say goodnight, señorita.' He gave her a brief bow.

'Señor——'

'Yes?'

'It was generous of you to send me the dress and slippers but I—I should like to pay for them.'

'You would then insult me!' His eyes glittered, he took a step forward, and in quick fear of him she held the stole against her and fled to the entrance of the hotel. She didn't look back. She had no need to do so. She knew he was smiling sardonically to have put her to flight.

She reached the suite in a rather breathless state and inserted the key in the lock of her bedroom door. She had her own entrance to the suite so she wouldn't disturb Mildred during the siesta hours, when her employer expected her to be out on some errand. Tonight she could only hope and pray that Mildred had not yet returned from the Casino.

She entered her room and switched on the light . . . and

46

at once from the adjoining room a voice called out:

'Is that you, Smith? How late you are! Come in here and explain yourself.'

Janna stood petrified. Her mind seemed to go numb and she couldn't think . . . if she had been able to she would have snatched off the stole, hurled it beneath her bed and waited for a propitious moment to return it to Mildred's wardrobe. As it was she was stricken by guilt at hearing her employer's voice. Her nerves had her at their mercy, shaken as they were already by Don Raul's revelations, and the way he had kissed her.

Before she could recover, the door swept open and Mildred marched in. She stared with hard amber eyes at her young secretary, taking in the soft disarray of her hair, the off-the-shoulder dress, and the honey stole draped against the silvery young figure.

'My mink stole!' she hissed, and Janna flinched as Mildred stormed across to her and snatched the fur away. 'You little thief! Creeping in, all dressed up in my finery! I bet that dress is one of mine.'

'No, it isn't.' Janna came alive again, and was surprised by her own vehemence. 'It wouldn't fit you, Mrs. Noyes, and I can show you the card that came with it. The dress was given to me . . . I'm sorry about borrowing your stole, but I haven't damaged it and I certainly meant to return it.'

'A likely story!' Mildred's eyes were blazing with spite. 'I'm going to call the police and lodge a complaint before you steal anything else. Decent people aren't safe with your sort around——'

'Oh, don't talk rot,' Janna broke in. 'I'm not a thief and you know it. I was a fool to borrow the stole, but I knew you wouldn't lend it to me if I asked. You're not a very charitable person, Mrs. Noyes. I've wanted to say so for a long time.'

'Have you, my girl?' Mildred's painted fingernails dug into the fur, as if she suppressed an urge to rake Janna's white skin with them. Her own skin was sallow and flushed.

'Well, let me tell you I've had enough of your sauce! I could get you locked up for taking my mink stole and that's a fact. You'll either apologise, or take your cards this instant.'

Janna stared at the woman for whom she had worked so uncomplainingly; who had never said a 'thank you' for any service rendered, and who hadn't the heart to forgive a young girl for being tempted by a fur stole for a few hours. She remembered the things that Don Raul had said; his frankness in pointing out that she was unappreciated by a selfish employer, and likely to remain so if she stayed with such a woman.

'All right, Mrs. Noyes,' she said resolutely. 'I'll take my cards and leave in the morning.'

'If you're going, then you can go tonight,' Mildred shrilled. 'You can go to whoever gave you that dress. Cinema date, indeed! In a model from one of the best shops? You look as if butter wouldn't melt in your mouth, Smith, but I've always guessed you were out to get yourself noticed by some man. Hasn't he yet forked out for a fur? You have to do more than smile for a fur, so here's your chance. Go to him right now and say you've nowhere else to sleep tonight.'

'But you can't turn me out,' Janna gasped. 'It's ridiculous —all over a stole you never wear. All over a few home truths. I've worked hard and patiently for you, and you treat me as if I've sponged on you.'

'I hired you to work for me,' Mildred snapped. 'Since you no longer intend to fulfil that function, then you can leave my expensive suite and go to your boy-friend. From the look of that dress he has money to spend, so go and ask him to support you. I've been a bit too generous to the likes of you, a little nobody from a charity home, and some typing pool in Piccadilly. I should have let you find your own lodgings, not had you here to share my suite and the hotel cuisine.'

'You had me here so you could keep me under your eye,'

48

Janna threw back at her. 'So you'd be sure I spent sixteen hours of the day at your beck and call, and bent over the typewriter pounding out love stories. All right, I'll go tonight, and if you find some other fool to work non-stop for you, then you'll be lucky. Not everyone is like me, Mrs. Noyes, grateful for small mercies and crumbs.'

She smiled, suddenly and rather recklessly. Crumbs from life's table, eh? For a change she would see about getting a little cake instead; it obviously didn't pay to be humble, no one seemed grateful if you worked hard for them. They merely sat on you, waited the chance to humiliate you, and thought you too much of a mouse to make a bolt for freedom.

'Perhaps you'll get my stamp card while I pack my belongings, Mrs. Noyes?'

Mildred's angry flush deepened. 'I'd never have thought you such a little chit,' she gasped. 'You might have some fool in tow at the moment—though what he can see in you I just can't imagine—but men soon feel like a change of diet, and then you'll be out on your ear, and it won't do you a scrap of good to come running back to me. I'm leaving the Côte d'Azur, so you'll be all on your own.'

Mildred spoke with such spiteful complacency that Janna just had to retaliate; she had to let the woman know that once she walked out of this suite it would be for good. Mildred hoped to scare her. She actually believed that she could make her mousey secretary beg to be kept on in a job that had become hateful to her. Janna couldn't stay! Anything was preferable to being one more day in this spiteful woman's employ.

'As it happens, Mrs. Noyes, I have been offered a situation in another country and I expect to be leaving fairly soon. Despite your suspicions I am not involved in an affair.' Janna tilted her chin. 'I'm sorry again that I borrowed your fur. It was a foolish thing to do and has taught me a very salutary lesson . . . in future I shan't expect or want kindness from anyone. I used to think it would be nice to find affection, after being deprived of it most of my life, but it's just a mirage. Everyone is out to please themselves. Self-interest is the byword these days and I've decided to make it mine as well. I'm fed up with being a mouse. From now on I shall scratch back when other people are catty to me.'

'You?' Mildred gave a laugh. 'You're a born loser, Smith. You've no talent, except as a typist. You've no beauty, no allure, nothing the men go for. You're nondescript compared to the other girls one sees on the Riviera.' Mildred flicked her eyes up and down Janna's slim figure. 'Men like curves and vivacity. They like to be flirted with and you wouldn't know where to begin. I bet this new job is about as exciting as a wet Monday. More typing in store, Smith?'

Janna longed to retort that in her new 'job' she was unlikely to see a typewriter, let alone handle one for hours on end, but on reflection she thought it wise to mislead Mildred Noyes. It wouldn't do for her to start snooping.

'As you said, Mrs. Noyes, I have little talent for anything else.' She swung on her heel and entered her room, where she began to pack her single suitcase. She would go down to Reception and book a room for the night; one of the cheaper sort. In the morning she would enquire the number of Don Raul's suite and tell him she had changed her mind about accepting his proposition. If he had changed his mind about taking her to Morocco, then she would be obliged to seek secretarial work, or maybe she would be bold and apply for a reception job in one of the many hotels on the Riviera. It would make a change, and in any event she could always find kitchen work if nothing else was available for Janna Smith, the orphan girl who had never known her real name and had been supplied with one by the Directors of the Essex Home For Destitute Children.

She took off the silver dress and slippers and replaced them with a suit and casuals. She ran a comb through her hair, snapped the locks of her case, and returned to the sitting-room. The room was empty. Her stamp card lay on the table, and she stowed it away in her bag. The door to Mildred's bedroom was firmly closed—the final snub, no goodbye for Janna.

Janna shrugged her shoulders and let herself out of the suite. She made for the lift, feeling no regrets at having quit her job. It was inconvenient to be turned out at one o'clock in the morning, but she wouldn't be refused a room.

The night clerk at the reception desk looked at her with suspicious eyes. 'We are all booked up,' he said coldly. 'There is not even a modest priced room available, miss. This is the busy season, you understand.'

He didn't know her, being the night clerk. He had not seen her with Mrs. Noyes, and Janna was obliged to tell him that she had left Madam's employ and been told to find other accommodation.

He looked unsympathetic. 'Most of our rooms and suites are booked in advance, and I am afraid I can't help you.'

'Could I spend the night in the lounge?' Janna asked. 'I wouldn't be any bother——'

'It is against regulations, miss. It is not permitted to allow the public rooms to be used at night. I am sorry.' He spread his hands, but was plainly not in sympathy with a girl who got herself dismissed from the employ of one of the hotel's wealthy clients. As usual, Mrs. Noyes was in the right because she was rich. Janna was the one under a cloud. She must walk out of the hotel and try to find a room elsewhere ... and it was so late. The other hotels might be fully booked, and she didn't fancy spending the night on the beach.

As she stood hesitant, the clerk turned to answer a call on the switchboard, and obeying instinct Janna spun the register towards her and scanned the names and room numbers. A certain distinguished name leapt at her and before the clerk turned round again she hastened to the stairs, ignoring the lift, and ran all the way to the third floor.

She was crazy to do this, but there was no one else she

could turn to. She pressed the bell of Don Raul's suite and waited with a thumping heart for him to open the door. Several minutes ticked by and she forced herself to ring the bell again.

All was silent along the carpeted corridor. Not a sound but the distant chirr of cicadas in the hotel gardens. What a situation to be in! Yet she would rather turn to the dangerous Spaniard than return to Mildred Noyes. She could face anything but that woman's crow of triumph.

Every nerve in her body gave a jolt as the door suddenly swept open and Don Raul confronted her, clad in a dark silk dressing-gown, his black hair ruffled from his pillow, and an amazed look in his dark eyes as they took her in.

He quirked an eyebrow at the suitcase she carried. 'You are going away and have come at this odd hour to bid me farewell?' he asked.

'I've been turned out by Mildred,' she blurted, 'and the clerk hasn't a room I can book for the night. I—I don't know what to do. It's so late and I don't fancy walking the streets——'

His eyes narrowed, then he put out a hand and jerked her inside his suite. He closed the door, and she stood breathless in front of his tall figure.

'I thought you might persuade the clerk to let me spend the night in the hotel lounge. You have influence, *señor*. I'm just a foolish girl who has lost her job.'

'You are in a pickle,' he mused. 'What happened? Did Madam pounce on you when you arrived home? Did you pluck up the nerve to defy her and got dismissed for daring to speak up for yourself?'

Janna nodded. 'That's almost exactly what happened.'

'Almost? Is there more?'

'I—I told her I had another situation to go to. I said I'd be leaving the Riviera altogether.'

'And she told you to leave tonight, eh?'

'In a manner of speaking. She was terribly annoyed.'

'No doubt,' he drawled. 'To lose a willing runabout

52

would annoy her. It amuses me to picture her face when you actually packed your bag and walked out.'

Janna gave a nervous laugh. 'It's all so ridiculous, like a farce or something. She could have let me stay till the morning, now here I am stranded, without a bed for the night.'

'Yes, what a predicament,' he said in that dangerous purr of his. 'And you come to me, when only an hour ago you ran from me as if a tiger were at your heels.'

Janna looked at him and told herself she had been a fool to expect anything but mockery from Raul Cesar Bey. 'I'm sorry I awoke you—I'd better go——'

'You had better stay,' he rejoined. 'I don't feel inclined to argue over the telephone with the night clerk, and there is a strong possibility that hotels in the area have a full complement of summer guests. Tell me, when you informed Madam Noyes that you had another situation to go to, had you Morocco in mind? Have you changed your mind about coming with me?'

'If you have not changed yours, *señor*.' Janna braved his eyes. 'I worked hard for Mildred Noyes and my reward was to be called a thief——'

'Why so?' he demanded.

'I borrowed her mink stole,' Janna said solemnly. 'You must have noticed it. I hoped she wouldn't be back from the Casino till late, but she evidently had a run of bad luck and returned earlier than usual. She was waiting up for me, and she accused me of intent to steal and made me feel so small. If I'd asked for the loan of the stole she'd have asked questions and then refused to lend it. I wouldn't care, but she never wears it.'

'She is a selfish woman, and envious of someone young who can look slim instead of bulky in a fur.' He placed an arm about Janna, took her suitcase with the other hand, and led her from the small foyer of his suite into the sitting-room. 'Sit down and I will pour you a small brandy. You look shaky.'

'I—I must admit I feel it, *señor*. I don't enjoy rows

with people, and she spoke to me as if I were a loose creature, or something.'

He laughed as he stood at the cocktail cabinet pouring brandy into a pair of globe glasses. Holding them cupped in his lean fingers, he crossed the carpet to where Janna sat deep in a soft leather couch.

'Drink this, Janna. It will settle your nerves and make the situation seem much less dramatic. A loose creature, indeed? Well, it won't matter if you stay here the night. You might as well be blamed for the act instead of the fiction.'

'What do you mean?' Janna's eyes were large and shocked, and the brandy glass almost slipped from her hand.

'You had better revive yourself with a mouthful,' he advised, his eyes upon her in a sardonic way.

She took his advice, and tried not to shrink away as he lounged on the nearest arm of the couch and inhaled his cognac.

'You have nowhere to go tonight, Janna, so I suggest you stay here.'

'I couldn't—not possibly!'

'I am sure you could.' His eyes smiled down into hers, wickedly. 'Wrapped in the cover from my bed, this couch should make a comfortable bed for you. I would offer you mine, but I don't want to frighten you away now you have braved the dragon and have come to me. Don't you know that when a desert man offers the protection of his tent he would never dream of betraying the trust of his guest?'

'This is not a tent in the desert.' Janna felt a trifle dizzy from the brandy and the events of this unusual night. 'If I were seen leaving your suite in the morning—well, you know what people are! It would be assumed that you and I——' There she broke off in helpless confusion, her cheeks flushed.

He tilted his brandy glass and savoured the contents. 'Only sticks and stones can break bones, *señorita*. Idle gossip can't hurt us if we know we are innocent as a pair of infants.'

She had to smile. He was the kind of man it was impossible to think of in those terms. If she left him in the morning as innocent as she came here tonight, then it would be because she looked too much like Joyosa, the girl who had fled from him. He had kissed her in the mimosa just to punish, and in comparison the tittle-tattle of other people was a small thing to bear.

'I—I have nowhere else to go.' She spoke drowsily, and longed all at once to put up her feet and give in to the softness of the couch and the forgetfulness of slumber.

'Off with your shoes and your dress,' he ordered. 'I will fetch a coverlet and a pillow, and you will sleep as sound as a child, and not worry about tomorrow until it comes.'

He strode into the other room, and she thought how kind he was being now she had given in to him. She was almost asleep when he returned with the quilted cover and a pillow. He stood beside the couch gazing down at her. She had removed her casuals and her jacket, but was still wearing her skirt. 'You will crease it,' he said drily. 'Come, don't be shy with me.'

She stirred as he touched her, her eyes flew wide open as he unzipped her skirt and pulled it off. 'Don't!' she gasped.

'It is done, Miss Smith. And I begin to suspect that it might be most amusing to coax you out of your shell.'

She grabbed the coverlet and wrapped herself in it, hiding her slip-clad figure from his gaze. He laughed and placed the pillow beneath her head. 'By this time tomorrow, you funny child, we shall be on our way to Morocco and you will never again see Madam Noyes.'

It was a nice thought. Never again to hear that bossy voice. Not to feel caged in with a typewriter and reels of tape recordings. Or to see other girls having fun with exciting men while she trailed in the wake of a large, booming figure and looked what she was ... a colourless typist, humbly certain that adventure and romance were not for her.

Morocco ... the golden sands of the desert ... herself in the hands of Raul Cesar Bey. Circumstances had made it almost inevitable that she be drawn into his life; into the strands of an intrigue that would unwind beneath the hot sun of El Amara. Yet despite her guilty doubts she was excited by the prospect of visiting a place that sounded so legendary. A desert city, ruled over by a real-life Princess, whose grandson and heir was the most dangerously attractive man Janna had ever dreamed of meeting.

Complications were bound to arise from such a game of make-believe, but all her life Janna had looked before she leapt ... this time she was going to leap first and if she landed in the soup it would be a most exotic one, a Moroccan *cous-cous* studded with plums both sweet and bitter.

She closed her eyes and drifted off to sleep, unaware that Don Raul came again to the side of the couch and studied her face against the pillow, his eyes intent and searching. In his dark silk robe, with the lamp slanting its light at an odd angle across his cheekbones, he looked proud and masterful. A smile moved his lips, and if Janna had suddenly awoken to see that smile she would have been alarmed.

She would have seen herself trapped in his eyes ... the girl from nowhere, who meant nothing to nobody, chosen because of a strange likeness to Joyosa to enact the role of his unwanted, unloved bride-to-be.

He put out the lamp and walked away from her, into his own room. The door closed and all was quiet, only the cicadas chirred in the dark trees, and the sleeping girl moved with a sudden restlessness, as if she felt an urge to throw off sleep and escape now, while she could, but soon she lay still again and her lashes were locked against her cheeks. A dream held her ...

And when she awoke sunlight was streaming into the sitting-room. Don Raul was standing over by the table pouring coffee, and looking active and lithe in a white polo shirt and a pair of rust-red slacks of immaculate cut.

He swung round to look at her, his lip quirking at the gamine picture she made with her hair tousled and her eyes big and startled. 'Good morning,' he said, bringing her a cup of coffee. 'I have to go out for an hour or two, and I want your promise that you will stay here in my suite. That you will not change your mind and run off to other employment now morning has come.'

She held the cup of coffee in both hands and gazed up at him. 'I don't think I have a free choice any more, Don Raul. You have taken charge of me, haven't you?'

'I am not abducting you,' he drawled.

She took a sip of coffee, and she couldn't have said if this were true or not. She knew only that she wanted to escape to a complete change of routine and environment; to meet people who were not overfed and selfish, spending their lives in enjoyment while others toiled for them. Whatever the outcome of this trip to the desert, Janna was sure of one thing ... she would see new things in a strange, exciting, colourful land, where the sands of gold surrounded the village of El Amara, and the House of the Pomegranate.

Don Raul glanced at his wristwatch, the leather strap dark against his brown and muscular arm. 'I have to arrange for our flight tickets to be booked, and I wish also to visit my cousin. I should be free by twelve o'clock, when we will lunch together and then go to Louis Jean for your new clothes.'

'My new clothes?' she echoed.

'But of course. You will, when we board our jet plane tonight, be the ward of a Princess and be dressed accordingly, and you will be wearing the Romanos emerald. In fact we will see right now whether it fits you.'

He strode to the bureau, unlocked a drawer and took from it a small velvet box. He returned to Janna and when he opened the box a dazzling ring was disclosed. He took it from the velvet and asked her to give him her right hand.

She couldn't move. She felt as if all the will-power had

57

left her limbs, and she could only watch numbly as he took her hand and slipped the ring on the third finger. It fitted as if made for her, the fabulous emerald ring of the Romanos family.

'What do you think of it?' he murmured.

'It's utterly splendid,' she gasped. 'So green and pure and yet full of fire. It frightens me a little, as if something terrible could happen because *I* wear it.'

He gazed down at her, his face thoughtful. 'You are sensitive enough to realise that the emerald has a history, you are not merely enraptured by its lustre and how it becomes a slender hand. It is placed on the right hand because for now it is merely a token; something the Princess wished me to present to her ward in the hope of an alliance between us.'

Janna listened to him with a sense of unreality. The flawless emerald and diamonds looked so strange on her hand.

'You must have a manicure at Louis Jean,' he drawled. 'My grandmother has sharp eyes, and she will be expecting someone chic, and a little pampered. I wonder if you can manage to look as if life has treated you like a pet?'

'Please tell me about the emerald, Don Raul. I'd like to know if it's a sad or a happy stone.' Then she glanced up at him and the breath seemed to catch in her throat. His eyes were glittering, as if with some intense emotion he barely suppressed. He plunged his hands into the pockets of his slacks and began to pace back and forth, the sun through the blinds striking gold and black across his tall figure, making him look like a caged tiger.

'An ancestor of mine received it as a gift from a Peruvian temple dancer, and it is said to bring good fortune only to the wearer who is pure as the stone itself. Many women have worn it down the years, Janna, and it has changed its setting several times, but still it holds a magic. Memories of the exotic dancer who loved a conquistador. Some of the Romanos brides have been happy enough, but there is also a history of sadness. Of young men of the family lost in wars, in clashes with authority, and in duels fought for the honour of a woman.'

He paused and stared into a bar of sunlight. 'It seems as if the stone has not yet found its true wearer, who could love as the Peruvian girl loved her Spanish soldier, throwing herself from the temple roof when he was ordered back to Spain.'

His eyes flashed to meet Janna's. 'There you have the story of the Romanos emerald; it is set down in the records of the conquistadors, a stone of love and tragedy.'

Janna was still sitting like a small statue when the door opened and closed behind Don Raul. She was alone with the ring, a token of deception, worn by her to bring him happiness with another woman.

CHAPTER FIVE

THE journey to Casablanca was for Janna a whirl of unusual impressions. They boarded the streamlined jet as dusk was falling, and her brand new luggage was stowed away with the more travelled cases of Don Raul. Her smart clothes and new hairstyle made her feel strange as they took their seats and he buckled the belt for her. Their eyes met as they were airborne.

'Relax,' he said. 'You look for all the world as if I am taking you to Morocco against your will ... that sheik of the desert abducting a girl for his pleasure.'

'It's been a strange and unreal sort of a day, *señor*. Selecting all those new things, going through the mysteries of the beauty salon, and running into Mildred just as we were leaving the hotel.'

He laughed softly, beckoned one of the hostesses and asked Janna what she fancied to drink. She glanced at the ring upon her hand, the emerald sparkling like a green eye, living and lustrous. 'A *crème de menthe,* please.' She had never tasted one and had a sudden longing to do so. The drink seemed in keeping with her new exotic role, and she watched with large, intrigued eyes as Don Raul ordered their drinks with worldly ease from the attractive air hostess ... who looked at him with admiring eyes. She had every reason to do so. He wore a grey lounge suit that off-set his air of distinction, and made his hair and eyes seem all the darker. He was the most striking man on the plane, and Janna sat beside him looking like his pampered property.

No one was to know that she was only hired to travel with him.

She wore a cream suit from Louis Jean trimmed with a whisper of fur. Her shoes and her bag were of matching snakeskin, her hair was softly scrolled about her slender face. Her fingernails and lips were a soft coral. She had no need to look in the mirror of the compact initialled with tiny jewels, which Don Raul had dropped casually into her bag. She looked a new person, and that was why Mildred Noyes had stared at her with maliciously accusing eyes in the foyer of the Splendide.

'*Buen prevecho.*' Don Raul raised his glass to her, and she murmured good health in return and sipped the misty green of her own drink, the ice cool against her lips. It was strange, but the further they flew from France, and the closer each mile brought them to Morocco, the shyer Janna felt, as if she had only begun to realise how much of a stranger was the man who had talked her into intrigue and dressed her in fine clothes to assist the part.

'Are you thinking of Madame Noyes and how she looked at us?' He leaned forward and his eyes were wickedly amused. 'What does it matter, what such a woman likes to infer from seeing you in the company of a man? It was gratifying that she be given a jolt of surprise. She could see for herself that you were not about to be tied to a type-writer.'

60

'No.' Janna smiled wryly. 'I'm sure she thought the very opposite; that I had sold my humble soul to Lucifer himself.'

'So?' His eyebrow quirked steeply. 'You regard me as a dark angel, eh? You think I have persuaded you to fall from grace?'

'Well, I wouldn't put it quite so dramatically.' She topped up her courage with another quick sip of her drink. 'But it was rather grim to have Mildred look at me from head to toe as if I had taken leave of my morals and become a Mata Hari.'

'You know what your trouble is,' he drawled, 'you have no confidence in yourself. Why should a man not uncover the snow to reveal the gentian? You remind me of the blue flower that grows on the lonely, snowy hillside.'

'I've been revealed for a reason,' she said, colour stealing into her cheeks. 'If I hadn't looked like Joyosa, you would not have bothered with me.'

'So be glad you have the look that caught my eye.' He ran his eyes over her. 'It pleases me that you wear good clothes with a natural grace. I wonder, Janna Smith, who your parents were? Did the orphanage never know?'

She shook her head. 'I was found in the stone niche where the Principal's milk was left each morning. There was no note attached to my shawl, only this gold chain bound three times about my wrist.' She showed him the chain which never left her wrist, to which was attached the little golden fish he had already noticed. 'When I left the Home they gave me the chain. It's all my worldly possessions.'

He gazed at her with eyes that were abruptly sombre. 'You have not had much of a deal, have you, Janna? The cold high walls of a charity house were yours; mine were the sunhot walls of a large desert villa. I was born on the edge of the desert. I grew up in the sun, under the burning blue sky, amid what is wonderfully wild and free. I can't imagine what it must be like to be imprisoned by rules and regulations, to sleep in a narrow iron cot, and not have the

Princess Yamila to run to with my boyhood discoveries.'

He fingered the chain on her wrist, and the little fish. 'All we have in common is that I lost my parents when I was still a child. We were travelling home by ship from a visit to Spain and were a few miles off Tangier when a fire broke out in the cargo section. Within half an hour the ship was aflame. My father kissed me, flung me into the water, and I swam away, thinking my parents would quickly follow. It was only later that I remembered my Spanish father couldn't swim, and I knew when I was at last picked up that my mother would have tried with all her heart to keep him afloat, only to drown with him. They were very devoted. If one had to die, then it were better they die together. Devotion should not be torn asunder.'

'I'm so sorry,' Janna was moved by his story, shocked by the imagery of a boy flung from a burning ship into the seething ocean. A boy so full of life, so strong even then, that he had battled all alone in the water until picked up; a lean, dark, vital boy, bursting into tears, perhaps, when landed at Tangier to await the parents who never came to him; who had gone together to a farther place.

'I had the Princess,' he said quietly. 'You had no family at all.'

'One gets used to it,' she assured him. 'It seems quite natural in the end to be alone.'

'It is unnatural,' he retorted. 'Birds rarely perch alone, fish swim in shoals, and something dies in the heart if there is no one to love. There has been no one, *chica*? No boy, no man? Ah, of course not. I knew it when I kissed you ... it was like holding snow in my hands.'

'I don't want to talk about that ...' She looked away from him, out of the window that revealed an infinity of star-shot darkness. Awesome to be so high in the night sky, one of ninety other passengers, and yet somehow alone with one man. A man who said devastating things, as if he had the right to shock her, to tear pity from her, to make her rebellious and submissive at the same time.

62

She hardly knew herself any more, a slim stranger in graceful clothes, her hand weighted by a fabulous emerald.

'Did you tell Rachael about me?' she asked.

'No.' A flame reflected in the window as he lit a cigarette. 'I merely told her that I was returning home and she was not to worry. I would see to it that my grandmother did not withdraw her financial support because of Joyosa. This time we parted without tears.'

Janna could picture their goodbye, the kisses that would be passionately tender instead of fiercely hurtful.

'I'm glad you kept all this a secret, Don Raul. I'm not proud of the part I've agreed to play. Suppose——'

'Suppose what, Miss Smith?' he taunted.

'Joyosa might turn up at El Amara.'

'I hardly think so. Did I not tell you that she finds me a sheik of the desert? She would be too afraid.'

'I think I could be afraid of you!'

'Do tell me why, Janna. It fascinates me to be let into your mind. Have I a wicked face?'

'You—you know too much about people,' she said defensively.

'You mean I am not easy to fool.'

'Impossible to fool, or mystify.'

'Ah, there you are wrong. I find you a mysterious person, Janna. Never before has my path been crossed by a young orphan girl who reminds me of a petal trapped in ice. I wonder what our desert sun will do to you? Will you bloom there, or melt quite away with apprehension?' He smiled, his eyes dark and glimmering through the smoke of his cigarette. 'You know, it isn't such a terrible thing that I ask of you, to pretend to be the sweetheart with no sweetness or heart to give me. You should enjoy the part. It should come natural to you to show only coolness to a man you disapprove of—ah, the blue eyes open wide! Not with a protest, but with surprise that I speak with such candour. I am a Spaniard, you know.'

'I know!' she echoed.

'And how could you approve of a man like myself, when you are a girl who has been taught to eat her crusts and be grateful for them, and not have the sins of pride and self-will. I have both, have I not? In your eyes, *chica*, I must be a sort of masculine Mildred, without the titian hair.'

'Of course you aren't.' Janna had to laugh. 'She's impossible—and so ready to think the worst of people without being an angel herself.'

'Only an angel may judge the faults of others?'

She looked at him quickly, detecting a note of irony in his voice. 'I'm no angel, *señor*. I didn't mean to imply that.'

'On the contrary, I find you are one of the few people who has a conscience. It worries you that people seem to care only about themselves. It concerns you that the pursuit of pleasure takes precedence over kindness and the will to help. I think, Janna Smith, that you will like very much the folk of El Amara. In them you will find a lot of kindness, and it will delight you to hear them chanting their old Andalusian songs in the fruit groves.'

'Andalusia is in Spain,' she said, puzzled.

'Quite so, and many of our people are descended from the Moors who lived in Spain for many years. One of my men has ancient keys that would open the doors of several large houses in Spain. Does it amaze you, *señorita*, to hear that the soul of Iberia sings on the edge of the desert? The Moors took their cultures and their traditions to the old country and implanted in Iberians the love of fountains and flowers, and enclosed courtyards where their women might be kept mysterious. Many lords of Spain are descended from the Moorish princes. My own grandfather married the Princess Yamila, who is a real daughter of Morocco. When I was a boy, she was still a ravishingly beautiful woman. Even yet she retains much of her beauty, as jade does, or a piece of carved ivory. You will be fascinated by her.'

'I shall be frightened, Don Raul, that she will find me an impostor.'

'Even if she does,' his smile was teasing, 'she will not have your head cut off. We are not that uncivilized.'

'It can't be passed off as a joke, Don Raul. I'm nervous.'

This seemed not to worry Raul Cesar Bey. His main concern was for the lovely Rachael, and Janna was sure it wouldn't trouble him if in the end she was sent away in disgrace from his grandmother's house.

'Decide now.' There was a sudden hard note in his voice. 'In a few hours we land at Casablanca, where I have booked rooms at a hotel. You come all the way with me, or we part there.'

'In a hotel garden?' she said whimsically. She gazed from the window into the darkness gemmed with stars. A beautiful night ... and all such nights would be so lonely again if she decided not to go all the way to the desert, to the house that stood there, white-walled and surely beautiful.

If she looked at Don Raul, into his dark, demanding eyes, she would be lost again, like a child who takes the hand of a stranger and hopes to be led homeward.

Where was home?

No more the orphanage, or the bedsitter in the heart of London. No more the hotel on the Côte d'Azur. Each one in its turn had seemed to lead to this moment, to flight across the sands to the gateway of a stranger's house.

Was it written in the stars ... or in the eyes of the man seated beside her?

She tensed as she felt his touch on the Romanos emerald on her hand. 'I offer you a trip to enchantment, little orphan.'

'It could turn out to be a mirage, *señor*.'

'I assure you El Amara is real, and for once in your life you will be treated like a princess.'

'I never went that far in my dreaming,' she protested.

'Most girls go that far,' he mocked. 'They even dream of a prince.'

She looked directly at him, a flash of defensiveness in

65

her eyes. 'I don't have silly dreams, Don Raul, or get crushes on men who are not of my real world. You needn't worry that I shall get so fond of the Romanos emerald that I shall want always to wear it. I can guess for whom it's really intended.'

He returned her look with narrowed eyes. 'Then you are a clever girl,' he said curtly. He spoke of impersonal things for the remainder of the trip, and it was a relief when the landing lights flashed on and they hovered over the airport. His hands felt brusque as he took hold of the buckles of her seat-belt and clicked them together.

'We have arrived at Casablanca,' he said.

They drove in a cab to the hotel, and were shown to rooms that turned out to be adjoining ones. After the bell-boy had left them, Don Raul said sardonically that the clerk must have assumed from his wire that the Princess would be with him. When in Casablanca together they always stayed at this hotel.

'It is of no consequence.' He smiled lazily. 'We slept last night in adjoining rooms.'

He glanced about the large, grand bedroom, and at Janna marooned on an oriental carpet. 'You look tired,' he said. 'Though it's late I feel myself like a walk to a restaurant that stays open late and serves Turkish coffee. Would you like to come with me, or do you want to go to bed?'

It was true she was rather tired, but she decided against going with him because she had the feeling he wished to be alone. All day they had been in each other's company and he had seen more than enough of her.

'I'll go to bed,' she said. 'Do we continue our journey in the morning?'

'Yes. We take the train to Benikesh, where a car will be waiting to pick us up. But you may like to stay there a day or two, to do a little sightseeing.'

'Whatever you wish, Don Raul.'

'Don't be humble.' He snapped the words and made her

jump. 'Benikesh is an old legendary city and I am sure you would enjoy seeing it.'

He bowed briefly and almost snapped his heels together as he left her and went into his own room. She walked to the dressing-table and winced to see how pale and tense she looked. So much had happened in so short a time, and she sank down on the dressing stool and allowed herself to droop a little now Don Raul was out of sight. He was so active and vital, and seemed never to get tired. Like the city beyond her windows, which still hummed with late-night sounds. As in London and New York there were people who seemed never to sleep. All night the neons burned with colour, spelling out the names of a thousand different things to be consumed or adorned by. They blazed above the sound of motor horns and music spilling from the clubs and late-closing restaurants.

Benikesh sounded much more like a desert city, and she looked forward to seeing the *souks* and the minarets, and the robed Bedouin who came in from the realms of sand, sunburned and free as hawks.

She heard a door close in the corridor and guessed that Don Raul was on his way out to his solitary supper. He was a strange man. There were times when he could charm her; others when he pounced and frightened her. She stared at her own face in the mirror and wondered if her likeness to Joyosa made him occasionally cruel to her. At other times he did unexpected things, such as dropping into her bag the white jade compact with the jewelled J. on the front of it. She was aware that Joyosa would possess such things, but all the same it thrilled her in a way she must guard against to be given such expensive trifles.

'For powdering that funny little nose,' he had said, and never before had anyone paid her a casual endearment, and she was beginning to understand why girls longed for love and affection from a man.

A thought that sent her spinning away from the mirror, which showed her a face that for Raul Cesar Bey was a reminder of someone for whom he had felt no love at all. It could have been that lack of love, sensed by Joyosa, which had sent her in flight with another man. To be the unloved bride of a man of pride and self-will, whom only love could tame, would be impossible. Joyosa had fled from that ... and Janna could hardly blame her.

She undressed, washed her hands and face, and climbed into the large silky bed. She reached up and pulled at the lamp cord. The room went dim, and then was lit at intervals by the neons that weaved a rose and green pattern upon the ceiling. She drifted off to sleep long before there was any sound from the adjoining room, any indication that Don Raul had returned from his jaunt. It may have been the strangeness of the place, or perhaps the flicker of the neons that induced the dream, one that recurred whenever she was worried about something; a reliving of a childhood incident, suffered in the grounds surrounding the Essex Home.

It was Christmas time. There were red berries on the bushes and the leaves were green and shiny. The children were out with a teacher, wrapped up in their woollies, collecting sprays of holly to decorate the rather austere hall where they would eat their Christmas dinner, and play games, and open the puzzles and books presented by the Board, substitutes for the toys that spilled so lovingly from a pillowcase in the small houses with gardens, where the children played who had parents to care for them.

There was a fairly wide stream running through the grounds, and because the weather was extra cold that winter it had iced over. Margie, one of the more daring youngsters in Janna's charge (Janna, then being thirteen, was a sort of prefect) noticed a lovely bunch of holly at the other side of the stream and darting away from the other children she slid across the ice and reached for her red glow of the berries, so warm and inviting on such a chilly day.

Suddenly there was a hiss and a crack. The ice had not yet set hard, and with a frightened scream Margie plunged into the icy water, a small orphan child quite unable to swim, her terrified eyes beseeching help of someone as the dark water closed over her pixie hood.

Janna had not known how to swim, but that had not stopped her from leaping in after the small girl and grabbing hold of her just as their teacher appeared. In the nightmare that followed Janna had nearly drowned as the teacher had got Margie to the bank of the stream, and then herself, half-choked by the freezing water, and later blamed for the incident because she was older than the children in her charge and she should have kept them from going near the iced-over stream.

Janna had cried herself to sleep that night, aware that if she had thought only about herself when Margie had fallen through the ice, the little girl might have drowned before their teacher heard the cries of the other children and came hurrying to the scene of the accident. Margie, with her pretty, mischievous face, was the one who was fussed over, and Janna had never forgotten being blamed.

Now in her dream it all came back, the terror, the feeling of being dragged under, the cries of Margie, and her own tears when it was all over and she was packed off to bed.

'It wasn't my fault ... she was in the water before I'd finished tying Tony's bootlace when it came undone ... please, I don't want to go to bed. Let me listen to the carols ...'

She was sobbing all over again, feeling the injustice of it all, and so hurt because they wouldn't let her listen to the carol singers from the village. 'I'll run away,' she sobbed. 'I can't stay here ... no one cares about me ... all I'm good for is to be a s-servant ...'

'Janna.' Hands gripped her, shook her, and she awoke with a cry, tears all over her face. She gazed up blankly at someone who was unfamiliar to her for several seconds. Her dream still gripped her, and she was a child again, alone in a dormitory where a single lamp burned low.

'Janna, you were crying out so pitifully ... something about running away.'

Then, with a thump of her heart, she knew who spoke to her, who held her, who looked down at her with such dark eyes in the lamplight. 'I—I was dreaming,' she murmured.

'Having a nightmare is more likely.' He sat down on the side of the bed, and his hands still pressed warmly into her shoulders. 'You have been crying, so it must have been a very unhappy dream indeed. Tell me, why do you want to run away? Because you feel guilty about posing as another girl?'

She shook her head, her hair tousled and damp like a child's. She raised a hand and wiped away her tears. 'It's something I remember in my sleep, every so often. Something that happened when I was a child at the orphanage.'

'Did they lock you in the broom cupboard for being disobedient?'

'N-nothing quite so drastic.' She gave a husky laugh. 'Silly of me to cry over the past.'

'Not at all.' His eyes held hers, the pupils enlarged and merging into the irises that were almost black. Wonderful eyes, in which she felt she was drowning. 'I used to have bad dreams when I was a child, and the Princess would come to me and hold me, and rock me off to sleep again.'

He smiled and Janna tensed as he drew her suddenly against him and cradled her in the hard hollow of his shoulder, covered by the black silk of his pyjama jacket.

'No ... please.' She struggled and was subdued and told not to be a little ninny.

'I'm not going to seduce you,' he mocked. 'I know what it is to feel desperately unhappy, and when this happens to us when we are young it is all the harder to bear. Now relax, don't think of me as a man, don't think of anything but falling off to sleep and having a good dream. The Princess used to say to me, "Think of your favourite book, *chico*, and in your dreams you will be the hero and able to overcome all your dragons." I say the same to you, Janna.

70

Be the heroine of your dreams, not the victim. If they shut you in the broom cupboard again, then just laugh and talk to the mops.'

This was kind, crazy, dangerous pillow talk. It made her want to cuddle close and let the world be well lost for love of him. Oh, what was she thinking, what was she feeling? This was the middle of the night, when everything took on a strange unreality, but it would be all too real in the morning if a little kindness from him led her to lose her head, and her heart.

'I—I think I shall sleep now,' she said faintly. 'I'm tired out.'

'Good.' With an unrevealing face he laid her back against the pillows, rearranged the silk coverlet, and rose to his feet. The lamplight slanted upwards and there was a hint of a smile in his eyes. 'What is your favourite book, Janna?'

'I just can't think—I've read so many.' Her smile was touched by mischief. 'Not one of Mildred's, anyway. More likely one of Scott Fitzgerald's.'

'Trying to pretend you are a sophisticate?' he mocked her, but not unkindly. 'Forget the old hurts, *chica*. Put them out of your mind and just remember you are here, far away from the orphanage and from Madam Noyes. Whatever sort of man I am, I don't think I am quite so terrible as that vain, noisy woman.'

Janna's toes curled together in the large bed ... he made her feel uncertain, but never inferior. He teased her innocence, but he didn't say things to make her feel small. If this were a dream and she had to awake to face Mildred again ... she shrank physically from the thought, and saw his eyes take on a glitter as he looked down at her.

'Am I so terrible, then?' he demanded.

'No,' she quickly denied. 'I'm grateful to you for not minding that I cried out and woke you with my nightmare.'

'I can be kind,' he drawled. 'Have you made up your mind to come with me to El Amara?'

She nodded.

71

'But you are still a little afraid, eh?'

'Haven't I reason to be?'

'Perhaps.' He walked to the door that stood ajar between their rooms. 'But we have a saying, don't count the bruised fruit before the harvest . . . don't hate or love blindly.'

'Some things are easier said than done, Don Raul.'

'You refer to the fruit . . . or the love?'

'I'm a stranger to love, señor. You said so yourself.'

'So I did.' He gave a sardonic laugh. 'But you will not remain a stranger to it. We love, or we become like hollow trees where the hornets build their stinging traps. Goodnight, Miss Smith. Forget yesterday and dream of tomorrow.'

The door closed behind him. She was alone, his words lingering with her, and she was more than ever certain that as the pretence ward of the Princess she was in for a complicated time at El Amara. She sensed that the Princess and her grandson were alike in their ways and their passions. She would be involved with the two of them, and she wondered if her nerve was up to it.

She put out the lamp and slid down between the bedcovers. What would it feel like to be no more a stranger to love? And who would be the stranger who would love her?

CHAPTER SIX

JANNA'S first impression of Benikesh was one of excitement, colour and noise. The big car that met them at the station had to twine itself around narrow streets and avoid laden donkeys, robed men walking in the road itself, and children who darted back and forth with all the fearless agility of young animals. They grinned when the driver of the car pressed loudly on the horn, leapt on the running board and pressed urchin noses against the glass to they might get a closer look at the girl inside.

She had to laugh. They were so amusing with their tuft of hair, which Allah used to handle if he wished to pluck any of them into heaven. And from the way they ran the streets and dodged among the traffic it was a wonder they didn't get run over.

The car came to a halt in the main square, alive with street vendors, and dominated by a mosque with a vivid green dome and a cluster of slender, latticed towers. The house they were to enter had a courtyard in which trees were hung with golden fruit.

'Bitter-orange trees,' said Don Raul, and she blinked in the hot sunlight as she glanced up at him. He wore a crisp white suit, and here in this vital desert city he seemed to take on a look that was more of the East and less cosmopolitan. Janna's heart missed a beat. He stood so tall, with the sun glinting on his hair that had the sheen of a raven's wing. He was tawny-skinned, and the faint slant to his dark eyes was intensified. He looked every inch the grandson of a Moorish princess, and people were hurrying out of the carved doors of the family mansion in Benikesh to do his bidding.

The luggage was lifted from the boot, a light was extended for his cigarette, and Janna understood not a word of the language that rattled around her in bursts of excitement.

'We will have something to eat,' Don Raul spoke to her in English, 'and then we will take a walk in the *souk*. As dusk begins to fall and they light the street lamps, there is a mysterious air about the place. The musicians start to play, and the snake-charmers work their magic. The Street of Spices is not to be missed in the fall of evening.'

'It sounds exciting,' she said, and was led by him through the cool mosaic hall of the house, with the sun slanting in patterns through the intricate screenwork of arched windows. They stepped out into a fountain court, and Janna caught her breath at the sudden peace and beauty after the bustle of the square.

Coffee was served to them, and they strolled about under the oleander trees and yellow melon flowers while they awaited the arrival of their meal. There were lush geraniums of a pure violet colour, and the twitter of birds among the Persian lilac. It was an Arabian Nights garden, and Janna felt as if she were dreaming. But it was real enough when she caught her heel in a tile of the court and might have fallen if lean hands had not steadied her.

'Th-thank you.' She flushed a little as she met his eyes. 'I'm so used to casuals that I feel strange in high heels.'

'You feel strange altogether, eh? Unsure of the man who has whisked you here on a magic carpet.'

'I—I thought we would be going to another hotel, señor.'

'Why should we, when this perfectly good house is used so infrequently now the Princess prefers to spend most of her time at El Amara? Are you worrying about the lack of a chaperone for the night? And you a girl from England, where such things are considered as out of mode as the Victorian stuffed furniture.'

'I'm not being stuffy.' She pulled away from him and sat down on the tiled rim of the fountain. 'You just seem full of surprises. I keep wondering what next you will spring on me.'

'That is the essence of the Spanish character, chica. You must also remember that I am part of this land of mystery.'

She dabbled her fingers in the water of the fountain, and was unaware that the sun lit to silver the fair tendrils of hair at her temples and the nape of her neck, and made her seem innocently young and rare in this garden where long ago the favourites of a Moorish prince had sauntered about. The tortoise that drowsed beneath a tree might have been the pet of one of those sloe-eyed girls in silk and anklets.

'I have only to look at you, Don Raul, to see you are not a beach lizard but a desert hawk.'

'Does it alarm you?' He took her hand, cool from the water, and held it to her pale skin contrasted with the bronze of his own hand. 'Snow and sun . . . they are not elements that mix. One of them can't help but lose itself in the other.'

She was compelled to look at him. 'Are you saying that I—I must melt to all your wishes, Don Raul? Now you do alarm me. I agreed to come out to your desert, but only on condition that I kept most of my independence. I hope you are not going to break your word now I am here.'

'What do you mean by independence?' he asked. 'The freedom to go and come as if you were in England? You must remember that now you are here, you are regarded as my grandmother's ward, and the girl most likely to marry me. Don't swallow me with your eyes! We know the true position, but other people don't. I may insist that you wear a light veil when we visit the *souk*.'

'You can't be serious?' But his eyes were. 'Don Raul, if you think I'm going out like an Arabian slave girl, then you're very much mistaken!' As she spoke she attempted to jerk her hand from his, and at once it was as if his fingers had turned to steel about her wrist. She stared at him, and read in his eyes his determination to have his own way.

'You will do as I say and not be childish about it.' He took in her sunlit hair, moulded about her head in soft pale curls. He studied each feature, and his eyes lingered on her sensitive lips. 'You are unusual to eyes accustomed to dark hair and olive skin, and I won't have it bandied about the *medina* that I allow the Princess Yamila's ward to be stared at as if she were an ordinary tourist.'

'You talk as if I were really your grandmother's ward. I—I'm only pretending, and not liking it too much.'

'All the same, from the moment you entered this house with me, the news was on the wing that I had with me the girl everyone thinks I have been waiting for. Most men in this part of the world marry as soon as they can, and it will now be assumed that I mean to marry you. The game has started, *chica*, and you play it to my rules.'

'Meaning I wear a veil in public?'

'Yes. A chiffon mask edged with beads.' He slowly smiled. 'Most attractive, as it happens, and many women of the

East cling to the veil because of its enticement.'

'I shall feel like a slave girl!'

'And is that such a terrible feeling?' he mocked. 'Come, Hussein is bringing our food to the table. I'm sure you are hungry after our journey.'

They ate in the shade of a wall, hung with a great cluster of scented mauve flowers. She recognised them as morning-glories, but even their familiarity could not dispel her feeling of strangeness; her lingering alarm that Don Raul was going to make her obey his wishes, and that her life would not be her own while she masqueraded as his grandmother's ward.

But it couldn't be denied that the food was delectable. Halved pink melon, crisping against her teeth with a sweet cool taste. Cobs of corn with butter melting on them. Rice in which chicken had been baked with raisins, onions, and chopped eggplant. A caramel custard that melted her, made it impossible for her not to smile at the man who had ordered the meal . . . who was used to giving orders and having them promptly obeyed.

'What lies behind your smile, I wonder?' He sank his teeth into a downy fig, but for once she wasn't going to tell him her thoughts. Those at least he could not command.

'How Mildred would have revelled in your Moorish garden, *señor*. What a setting for a novel all this would make!'

'A setting for romance, do you mean?'

She answered him with a cool look, refusing to be drawn into a subject which held elements of danger. Not for the first time had she glimpsed in his eyes a certain disturbing look, as if he were intrigued by a girl who had never had a romantic affair with a man, and would like to test her reaction to an assault on her emotions.

'That was a delicious meal, Don Raul.'

'I noticed how you enjoyed the food, Miss Smith.' His eyes flicked over her. 'And yet from the look of you a man might suppose that you lived on wild honey. Did you really get enough to eat when you were a child?'

A ripple of laughter escaped her. 'I suppose I must seem a

hank of hair and bone to you, *señor*. I believe Spanish men like women to be pigeon-plump and raven-haired.'

'There are exceptions to every rule,' he drawled. 'With regard to Joyosa several of my Moorish friends suggested that I feed her on sweets and cream cakes, as they do in the *harems* when a girl is not as plump as would be wished.' With a wicked glint in his eye he pushed towards Janna the date and nut fondants which had been brought with their *mocha* coffee. 'Will you have a sweet, *chica*?'

'Are you more a desert man than a Latin one?' She took a sweet and nibbled it. 'I begin to think so.'

'Are you more a woman than a little saint? I begin to wonder.'

'I am the typist you hired to be an actress, and I'm sure it doesn't worry you how wicked I begin to feel now I am here and have to behave as if I've always been pampered and waited upon.' She watched an orange butterfly preening itself against a melon flower. She was a scared young girl, not a woman who knew how to handle a spirited male. She was quivering inside, as vulnerable as that butterfly that hung by a wing to a petal.

'Is there not a little fun in pretending to be a man's pet?' he asked quizzically. 'Come, it must give you something of a thrill to be indulged and spoiled for a change.'

'I might grow too used to being spoiled, Don Raul.'

'Then I must keep my eye open for a rich and indulgent husband for you, to save you from falling into the clutches of another Mildred when we part.'

'Really?' She laughed, but it hurt for some odd reason. 'Do you regard riches as the main requirement for marriage, Don Raul? I may have other ideas.'

'Such as?'

He was goading her to the obvious reply, but she wasn't falling into his trap. 'I may wish to open a tea-shop, or take training as a beautician. It was all rather fascinating at the salon the other day.'

He smiled at her reply and leaned back in his cane chair,

the swarm of mauve flowers all about his dark head and his broad, white-clad shoulders. 'You may surprise yourself and fall in love, *chica*. It is the most basic of drives, and has been known to attack the most guarded of hearts. What will happen to your tea-shop if you fall head over heels in love with someone?'

'I shall have to think about that event if and when it occurs,' she said lightly. 'Mildred always said I was a born spinster, and lots of shy people do become married to a career rather than a person.'

'Are you very shy?'

She avoided his eyes, so bold and amused by her. This, she thought desperately, was turning into one of those dangerous talks she had hoped to avoid. It was unfair of him to start it, as if he were tempted to uncover her young, formless, secret dreams.

'Was Joyosa shy?' she fenced. 'If she wasn't, then your grandmother is going to wonder about the change when she meets me.'

'The Princess met Joyosa only twice before, and that was when the girl was a child. Does it seem appalling to you that so young a girl should be chosen for a man like me?'

'I—I don't know how to answer such a question, *señor*.'

'I am sure you do, *señorita*.' He closed his lean fingers around a mauve flower and slowly crushed the petals, and all the time he looked at Janna in her simple dress. She had removed the jacket and her arms were bared but for her wrist-chain, with its lucky fish. 'Did you not say that you could understand a girl being afraid of me? Afraid of what, I wonder? My temper . . . or my passion?'

'I think you could be cruel . . . impatient towards some women,' she said bravely.

'Do you include yourself in that category?'

She watched his ravishment of the flowers, the falling petals, the look he had of always bending others to his will. Only with the Princess would he use the velvet glove. Janna herself had already felt the steel in his grip.

'Yes,' she said, 'I think I do.'

'Then how daring of you to put yourself in my hands.'

'I shall probably live to regret being so impulsive.'

'The cosy tea-shop in a small resort on the English coast should compensate for any alarm I cause you, in the course of our pretence relationship,' he drawled. 'I can't promise to be predictable, but I think you will enjoy living on the edge of the desert. It will be for you an experience never dreamed of, to wander in a palm garden, to see a tawny moon rising over the sands, to hear the dawn wind whispering to you to rise and ride . . . perhaps with me.'

'But I can't ride,' she gasped

'Then I will teach you,' he said calmly

'There must be several things which I can't do . . . things people will expect of Joyosa. I can't speak Spanish——'

'Don't get in a panic.' Swiftly he was on his feet and striding round the table to her. He jerked her to her feet and held her in the hands which had crushed the flowers. To be so close to the dark strength of him, to the passion and the danger, was enough to alarm anyone, and Janna had not forgotten the feel of his warm, hard lips on hers. He was unpredictable, and she was unprotected. An explosive combination.

'As I told you, Joyosa had an English mother so she speaks good English. Other matters can be dealt with quite easily. You will learn to ride early in the mornings, when I shall also teach you a little Spanish. Remember, it will not take a year and a day for us to show the Princess that you are not madly in love with me. As soon as she realises that I would have a snowdrop for a future wife, you may melt out of my life, *chica.*'

Melt was the word . . . she felt in danger of it right now, for consciously or not he was holding her so that her slim body was pressed to him, her wrists gripped at the back of her, his darkly handsome face so near that her quick breath must have touched his skin.

'Joyosa never had such large and speaking eyes,' he mur-

79

mured, making no attempt to release her from such a defenceless attitude. 'Look at me like that in front of my grandmother and she will soon be convinced of your dislike of my touch.'

'I—I don't like to be gripped like some tame rabbit. Don Raul, you're hurting me——'

'Little liar!' His eyes laughed down into hers. 'You dislike me for being an arrogant devil, and when I touch you, *niña,* you are unsure of what my next move will be. You are afraid I might lower my head a little more and so bring my lips nearer to yours. Don't you like to be kissed?'

'Not by you,' she gasped. 'It's just a game to you. A cat and mouse game. All your life you've done more or less as you please, while I'm someone who has been restricted. You're curious to see how I react now you've let me out of the mousetrap. Perhaps you think I should show my gratitude by letting you . . . make love to me?'

'Are you that grateful?' he asked wickedly.

'I'd sooner wash dishes!' she retorted, and at once his grip tightened on her hands and she was drawn even closer to him. A bruising kiss seemed imminent . . . and then to her unspeakable relief Hussein came out from the cool shadows of the house, a white-clad, deferential figure, eyes veiled as he made himself noticed by Don Raul.

They spoke in Arabic, and then Hussein bowed his head and withdrew. Don Raul held Janna's rebellious gaze with his. 'This time you get away with a remark I'd like very much to punish. I have a business caller, so would you like to remain here in the garden, or shall Hussein show you to your room, where you can take a siesta while I am detained?'

'I'd like to stay here,' she said, rubbing her wrist as he let her go.

'Did I really hurt you?' He smiled heartlessly at the action. 'Or is it the touch of my hands you are trying to erase?'

She watched him stride away from her into the house, a

tall, supple figure, etched a moment beneath the sculptured archway, and then gone from sight. The fountain court seemed to fall curiously silent, and yet it wasn't really so for the water still tinkled in the stone basin, the birds still twittered in the bird-pepper trees hung with scarlet fruits, and the bees hummed in the oleanders. Lush pink oleanders, with dark roots in which ran a sap which could cause pain and suffering.

Janna shivered in the sunlight and wandered away from the table she had shared with Raul Cesar Bey. She continued to rub her wrist-bone, the one into which her gold chain had pressed, leaving a small pink mark. She came to an archway leading into yet another section of this Moorish garden, and wandered along a path shaded by myrtles. A pool glimmered, a breeze whispered, petals drifted from a tangle of roses. She gave a start as a frog jumped in the lily pool, a shiny green splay of legs on a pad of leaves.

He looked like a little dragon crouching there, and she smiled to herself, remembering the fable of the prince who was turned into one; who could only be released from the enchantment by a girl who saw him with loving eyes.

It was this garden, a secret place of sunlight and shadow, that made her think of fables . . . and of love. She imagined that if a girl loved a man, he became in her eyes a person of extra dimension. He might be a devil, but to the girl in love with him he would seem a god.

The breeze sighed, or was it herself? She wanted someone to be devastatingly kind to her, without motive, without anything but the desire to please her. How lovely. Nicer than the nicest gift. Warmer than the warmest fire. To see just once in her life a pair of eyes kindling for her alone.

All at once she became aware of sounds beyond the high wall enclosing the garden. She listened, and saw a small door half concealed behind a mass of flowering vines. She pushed aside the living curtain and tried the door. It opened, and there was the city square, the towering mosque, and the narrow alleys that meandered around it, forming the *souk* that was already lit here and there by a yellow flame in a brass lamp. The stalls were packed close together and their mat coverings formed a winding arcade. Articles glittered and gleamed in the shadow of the awning, and robed figures moved back and forth like figures in a medieval painting.

There was a sound of strange music emerging from the heart of the place, and Janna thought of snake-charmers, and sellers of spices, red pomegranates, and Arabian silver.

She dismissed with a little laugh the idea that she must wear a veil before she dare venture into the *souk*. That was just another of Don Raul's sardonic jokes. He knew that a European was not expected to behave like a Moorish woman . . . why, even they were allowed to go unveiled into the streets if they wished, but lifetime habits were not easy to break and Janna saw several figures go flitting by, making mystery with one eye revealed, the rest of their person swathed in the *baracan*.

Suddenly she was seized by the spirit of adventure and knew she must take a look at the *souk*. It had such an intriguing air, and Don Raul might be kept so busy that he wouldn't find time, after all, to show her around. She darted back to the patio for her jacket and purse, and five minutes later was crossing the square towards the enticing noise and mystery of her first Arabian market. She told herself she wouldn't venture too far into its winding alleyways, but just far enough to get the feel of the atmosphere, and to purchase some small memento of her visit.

Dusk was falling quickly now, and the yellow lamps were springing alight along the lanes of stalls. They lit the dark eyes of the vendors, and made more colourful the heaps of wares and vegetables. The throaty language mingled with the bursts of music, and Janna felt a sudden panic as she entered the place and found herself in a throng of strangers and swept along on the tide of shoppers, idlers, and bargain-hunters.

Soon, however, her nervousness was overcome by the

fascinating displays set out on every side of her. Handwoven silks of every colour and so soft to the touch. Rugs in bright Arabian designs. Hammered jewellery and strings of beads. Silver bird cages. Heaps of symbols in the shape of fish, stars, and the Hand of Fatima.

Mounds of mint sent out a tang that mingled with smoking *kebab*. Pumpkins towered over purple figs and sweet lemons. Apricots and henna were piled beside slippers of soft leather, and gorgeous stuffs for bride dresses were surrounded by chattering women. The scent-sellers displayed their wares in the tiniest phials, and the most ornamental flagons, but Janna's eye was caught by a little box in the shape of an ark.

She picked it up and at once the vendor rattled out a price which she guessed to be ridiculously high. She shook her head and offered ten dollars for the box. He threw up his hands in horror, and she pointed out a dent in the lid. He shrugged and lowered the price to thirty dollars. Janna at once replaced the box on the stall.

'Twenty-five dollars,' he choked, and his swarthy face looked cunning within the cowl of his *burnous*.

Janna traced the patterns with a fingertip. 'Fifteen,' she said, and felt quite pleased with herself for having the nerve to bargain with the man.

His eyes glittered, taking in her clothes, and her fairness of hair and skin. 'Twenty,' he said obstinately.

'Okay, keep it.' She turned away, and at once let out a startled cry as his hand grasped her by the shoulder.

'The *romi* rich,' he said loudly.

'I am not!' She threw off his hand, and her face whitened as the crowd of people seemed to press in upon her. Their eyes seemed hostile, and the musk of their robes caught in her throat. She glanced around her and felt she had to get out of the crowd before it trampled her. She opened her purse with shaking fingers and was about to pay for the box when a hand closed on hers and the purse snapped shut.

She glanced up wildly and found herself looking at a tall

cloaked figure. 'Oh . . .' The word broke from her as the crowd melted away, and the stallholder retreated behind his pile of brass and copper wares.

Fingers gripped her elbow and she was hustled along the lanes until they reached the square, with the lamps of the mosque casting patterns of gold upon the walls and roofs of the houses.

'I should bend you over my knee and give you a spanking, but I think your encounter with that rogue has taught you a lesson. What did you intend to do with that piece of junk you were buying?'

Her nerves still felt shaken by the incident, and she felt so mortified that *he* of all people should have had to come to her rescue. 'I liked it . . . it was unusual.'

'You are like a child, with about as much sense. I suppose you thought it clever to go alone into the *souk*? I shudder to think what other trouble you could have got into if I had not been there.'

'You're much cleverer, aren't you?' She felt furious with him for finding her embroiled in an argument over a worthless brass box. Her cheeks tingled. In the folds of his Arabian cloak he had followed her through the twisting lanes of the *souk*, waiting for her to get into some sort of trouble so he could act the superior male. 'I hope you enjoyed spying on me?'

'My visitor had just left and I was about to come out to the patio when I saw you snatch up your coat and go hurrying out into the street. I followed you, naturally.' The strange light of the square was caught and held in his eyes, as she was held by his steely fingers. 'Are you impulsive, foolhardy, or inspired to annoy me? If so, then we are not going to be very good friends.'

'I thought cool indifference was what you wanted of me, Don Raul. Some part of our act should at least be genuine.'

'You are trying my patience, Janna.'

'Why, because I won't be cowed by you?'

'I expect you to behave with a reasonable response to my

orders. I don't make them just to be tyrannous. I make them for your own good. This is Morocco, let me remind you. Here you are a young stranger, and in the *souk* you were obviously frightened when you became the centre of a crowd of people so unlike yourself. Most of them were merely curious, but there were no doubt others who thought you alone, who might have decided to rob you of your purse . . . or even your innocence.'

'W-what do you mean?'

'You know well enough what I mean.'

'Such a thought never entered my head!'

'Then allow it to do so in the future. You seem unaware of the fact that you are no longer a little typist trailing in the shadow of a noisy novelist. You now wear attractive clothes, the sheen in your hair has been brought out, and upon your hand you wear the Romanos emerald.'

'The emerald!' she gasped. 'Don Raul, I never gave it a thought—oh, it might so easily have been stolen! No wondere you're annoyed with me.'

'Over the emerald, eh?'

'I—I never realised. I'm unused to wearing something so valuable. Please, won't you keep it yourself just to be on the safe side?'

He raised her hand and studied the rich glimmer of the stone in the lamplight of the city square. 'You are an unusual girl, Janna. So you quite forgot you were wearing my ring?'

'I'm afraid so——' And then she glanced up into his face and felt her heart give a painful twist. The woman he loved should be wearing the ring, but instead it masqueraded on the hand of someone who meant little to him. He had not followed her into the *souk* because he feared for her safety. He had been keeping an eagle eye on the emerald ring that she wore.

'All's well,' she said brightly, 'the ring has come to no harm, and I'll be more careful of it in future, if you insist that I go on wearing it.'

'I do insist.'

She smiled. 'How fascinating the mosque looks with lamps glimmering through the lattices. It glows like a great jewel itself. Are visitors allowed up there on the balcony that encircles the tower beside the dome?'

'Would you like to go up and view the city from the *muezzin* tower? I warn you the climb is a steep one.'

'It would be an experience——'

'You seem very eager to experience everything in one day.'

'Don't we leave tomorrow for El Amara?'

'Do you wish to?'

'Don't I have to bow to your wishes, *señor*?'

'Not in every single thing, *señorita*.' His tone was dry. 'We can stay another day, and this time I will take you to a dealer of genuine antiques and you may choose a jewel box of real value.'

'I—I wanted only a memento of my visit to Benikesh.'

'As if you were taking home an ashtray or a stick of rock from the seaside?'

'I suppose so.' His hand had slackened and she edged away from him. 'There's no need to laugh at me. I certainly couldn't afford a genuine antique.'

'You would not have to buy it yourself.'

'I would prefer to.' She tilted her chin. 'It isn't nice to keep taking presents, and they mean so little to you because you can buy whatever you please. You don't know the thrill of buying some small thing just for the pleasure it gives. You're spoiled, Raul Cesar Bey.'

'And you are unspoiled.' His voice went dangerously soft, and she found herself not free at all but enveloped suddenly in the swirl of his cloak. 'Come, we will climb to the tower of the mosque and you may wish upon a star. I daresay that will please you more than any jewel.'

'Yes.' She felt curiously breathless as he strode with her across the square, holding her close to his side so his cloak enfolded her.

The night was drenched in the aromas of this desert city,

and the stars hung low in the indigo sky. What would be her wish? And did this place hold magic enough to make it come true?

Inside the dimness of the mosque they had to discard their shoes for slippers without heels, and these made the steep climb to the tower rather hazardous. Janna bent suddenly and removed hers. She ran ahead of Don Raul on nyloned feet, up and up the stairs to the stars, out upon the narrow balcony with its latticed railing. The wind came at her and she caught her breath. A desert wind, blowing in from those wide and limitless spaces, across which she would travel to a house in a pomegranate grove.

Her breath escaped in a little gasp as a tall cloaked figure came to the parapet and they gazed together at the big Arabian stars, tawny and glowing, there to be plucked, or so it seemed, but when Janna stretched out her hand she found it empty.

'So lovely,' she breathed. 'A city of magic and out there beyond the walls a thousand leagues of sand. It frightens me a little. A world so different from mine, and yet you've known it all your life and can have no fear of its strangeness. No fear of anything really.'

'I should not have bothered with you if you were the sort who developed the vapours at every mishap,' he said. 'You are not without nerve.'

'I shook a bit in the bazaar,' she chuckled, and her annoyance with him had died away, was forgotten up here, where one was conscious of greater things than petty angers.

'The stars are like people,' he murmured. 'Though they seem so close together in the sky, they are really far apart. Each star is lonely.'

'Yes, one feels that.' She glanced at him and saw his profile outlined strong and forceful against the starlight. Was he feeling lonely for the woman he had left behind in France? Was he wishing that she were here beside him . . . instead of a girl who resembled Joyosa? Her gaze fell to his hands, clenched on the rail, the knuckles agleam against the bronze skin and the black iron.

He no more relished a game of deception than Janna, but he found it a necessity. He could not fight with the frail Princess Yamila . . . he needed Janna to play the part of Joyosa; to enact the lack of love he had found in the girl chosen to be his bride.

Janna gazed at the stars that blazed over the desert. Their warmth was too far away and she gave a slight shiver and wished she might be enfolded again in the cloak of Raul Cesar Bey. It would not be easy, what he asked of her, to pretend she was indifferent to him. She had never been more aware of anyone as in this moment upon the balcony of an Arabian tower.

Janna had never known love or tenderness. She had learned young the meaning of inner loneliness, but here on the edge of the desert she became aware of what love could mean; how much joy it could bring if felt in all its depth by two people.

But at El Amara she must hide what was growing in her heart, and act the ice-maiden. That was what Don Raul asked of her . . . a coolness to convince his grandmother that a girl-bride was not for him.

CHAPTER SEVEN

THEY were to make the journey to El Amara by safari car, and it wasn't until they were on the point of departure that Janna learned it would take two days and they would spend a night in the desert. Don Raul seemed unconcerned by the conventions that ruled Latin lives . . . he was much more a man of the desert. It had angered him that she should go unveiled into the *souk*, yet he spoke quite casually of this desert journey that would involve them in a rather compromising situation.

They would be so alone, and when she looked at him with this reflected in her eyes, he smiled in that half-mocking way of his, an eyebrow peaked against his bronzed skin.

'Shall we take Hussein with us, or do you trust me to behave like the perfect gentleman?'

'You aren't perfect, *señor*, except in one sense.'

'And may I know what that is?'

'You may not.' She was flushing slightly as she turned away to adjust her sun-glasses. He wore an open-collared pale tan shirt with matching slacks, and his desert shoes made his walk even more silent and pantherish. It was the look of him that was disturbing.

He walked around the car, examined the engine, made sure they had plenty of water, and a spare tyre. The car was tough and built to travel across the sands. Their luggage was loaded, and there was a wicker hamper of food, a pair of sleeping-bags, and a revolver which he slid into a pocket beside the driving seat. Janna did not comment on this. She was level-headed enough to know that certain dangers lurked in the desert . . . poisonous snakes, wild jackals, and sand-cats large enough to rip a person to pieces.

'I think I have made a thorough check of everything.' He stood with narrowed eyes a moment, and then he glanced keenly at Janna. 'You wish Hussein to travel with us?'

She shook her head before she realised the significance of her reply. Her heart shook a little. 'Unless you want him along,' she added hastily.

'He has a young family here in Benikesh. I should hate to drag him away from them just for the sake of one night in the desert . . . wouldn't you?'

'It would seem unnecessary,' she agreed.

'Quite.' His tone was dry. 'We are not about to spend the night guiltily. You noticed there were two sleeping-bags?'

'Please——' The word broke from her, and she was glad her eyes were concealed behind smoked glasses. They might look more hurt than shocked, for it hurt to love a man who was tempted not by her charm but by her naïveté. It amused

89

him that he could taunt her to a blush with one of his audacious remarks. 'Orphan Annie isn't used to sophisticated company, *señor*. You must forgive me for being so prim and proper.'

'You are forgiven, *chica*.' He re-entered the house for something, leaving her to gaze at the minarets of the mosque, and at the archways perfect for framing palm trees and stately robed figures. A city of sun-bleached walls, of wooden balconies that jutted over narrow streets, and a smell of ripe spicy fruits and stews. Exciting and yet like a mirage that had slipped in and out of her life. The burning reality, the memory she would carry away with her, was of starlight over the city, and the wind snatching her breath as she awoke to love and knew it would bring her trouble rather than joy. Every moment, every glance, everything shared with Don Raul would be a bit of heaven and a bit of hell, and yet she wouldn't have missed any of it to be again the nonentity Mildred had made of her. This, at least, was living.

Already the warmth of the morning had grown stronger, and as Don Raul returned to her side she braced herself for the journey ahead. She had no illusions about the desert being beautiful under the sun; she knew the sands were cruel, especially to a novice.

Don Raul carried a small leather satchel in his hand. 'This is a first-aid kit,' he said. 'I know I am acting as if we are setting out on a safari, but the desert is an unexpected place. Anything might happen, and it can do so in the flicker of an eyelid. I hope I am not alarming you, *chica*?'

'Not at all.' She smiled, though she felt the stirring of her nerves as his arm brushed hers. 'I realise that the desert is vast and unpredictable. I'd hate to be lost in it.'

'Even that could happen,' he warned, 'if a *sirocco* blew up and covered all landmarks, or I ran the car into one of the gulleys that lurks like a greedy mouth in the sands. Because I know the dangers, we take more water than we shall need for the journey . . . only a few weeks ago a couple were

90

stranded when their car broke down. They were Americans and had stocked up on Coca-Cola but not on water. A burning desert thirst is more intense than any other kind, and the only thing that slakes it is the pure aqua, so you can imagine the torment of those people. By the time a band of nomads found them, they were so exhausted as to be almost dead.'

Janna shuddered. 'You . . . you don't spare my feelings, *señor*.'

'No. I don't believe in anyone harbouring romantic notions about the dangerous things in life. They must be faced with the eyes wide open, and if they can still be loved, despite their menace, then life has increased in excitement.' His eyes held Janna's, and then a glint of a smile crept into their darkness. 'But I won't disillusion you completely. The desert as night begins to fall is the most lovely place on earth. And at dawn, as the desert awakes to the touch of the sun, one can believe that in the Garden of Allah the first man and woman fell in love. Make no mistake, Janna. Once you have known the desert, you are never again free of its strange enchantment. It haunts you when you are away from it. It calls you back with a siren's voice.'

'I'm a female,' she said demurely. 'What sort of voice does the desert use to call a woman?'

'How would I know that?' At once the light in his eyes became a wicked one. 'You will have to tell me when you have heard it.'

Confused by the purr in his voice, and by the strong brown throat in the opening of his thin shirt, she turned to the car. 'Are we ready to leave, *señor*?'

'Yes, let us be off. You have all your belongings?'

She nodded and slid across the wide front seat to her place beside the open window. The top of the car was of canvas, which would make shade and draught as they drove across the desert. The slightest bit of coolness would be more than welcome once they were out under the hot sun.

'You have forgotten your *hiriz*?'

She glanced at the tiny gold crescent that hung now with the gold fish on her wrist-chain. He had bought it for her when they emerged from the mosque to find an old, cowled seller of charms sitting on the steps. 'No, I have it safe. I do believe you're superstitious, *señor*.'

'I am the son of a Spaniard and the grandson of a Moorish princess,' he drawled. 'What else do you expect in a man of two nations so steeped in the lore of fate and *Kismet*?'

'Then you believe that everything hinges on fate, *señor*, and that whatever happens to us is inevitable, like the tide drawn by the moon?'

'Don't you believe it, *chica*?' Now he was driving along a narrow street, their wheels bumping over the ancient cobbles, the horn warning every few yards a jay-walking citizen of Benikesh. 'It could not be a thing of chance that we met at a moment when I needed to solve a problem close to my heart. Your resemblance to Joyosa was so uncanny, there in the mimosa. I thought for a moment that she had come back into my life.'

'And you wouldn't wish her to return, *señor*?'

His answer was in Spanish, and the curt tone of his voice imparted the full meaning of the words. Janna flinched, and felt as if she were included in his dislike because of her likeness to the girl who had fled from him and the Princess, afraid of his background and life in a desert house. Janna sighed, and felt his glance as the safari car turned out of the gates of Benikesh.

'Are you sorry to be leaving?' he asked.

'The place has a certain battered glamour, *señor*.'

'Wait until you see El Amara . . . a jewel of a place. The Princess has striven to make it so, and I have not been idle myself. We are not despots, she and I, living off the people and the land.'

'Have you no sisters or brothers?'

'I have some cousins who live at the house.'

'And they have met Joyosa?'

When he nodded, Janna grew anxious again. 'I—I wish

I were going to El Amara as a guest instead of a fake.'

'What if you were going as yourself, Janna, without any pretence?'

She shot him a wide-eyed look, and he went on: 'The Princess might be so intrigued by you that she may forget her schemes with regard to Joyosa. It was never a settled thing. What she really desires is to see me with someone I might marry.'

Janna's heart beat quickly. 'But what of Doña Rachael? You spoke of finances; that a breakdown in your grandmother's plan to have you marry her ward might make things awkward for Joyosa's sister.'

'It would have done so if I had returned home alone, with no fair young thing to parade as my possible bride. My grandmother's anger will be softened by you, *chica*. She will be able to take an interest in you . . . a shy English girl with the complexion of a pale rose, and eyes so wondering and blue. You will be like a new toy for her. She will make plans, but after a month or so you will pretend tedium, a home-sickness for England, and we will agree amicably to cancel the arrangement. No one need be hurt.'

'It sounds reasonable——'

'And much to your liking, eh? You need tell no lies.'

'I—I hated the thought of a barefaced deception.'

'Little Miss Prim!' he laughed. 'It is agreed, then, that from now on we are unofficial lovers. I have taken you on the rebound, because of your likeness to Joyosa, and so we make the Princess happy, we make Rachael secure, and we make Janna greatly relieved not to have to act a part.'

'And what of you, Don Raul?'

'I shall just enjoy myself.'

'I don't quite understand——'

'There will be a little more kissing,' he said wickedly. 'A little more show of affection . . . until the time comes when you wish to be set free.'

'Is it necessary?' she gasped.

'You are not compelled to enjoy it,' he taunted. 'But if

we switch our plan, and if my grandmother is to be convinced that you appeal to me, then now and again you will have to brace yourself for an embrace. Do you shrink from it?'

'I expect I shall manage to tolerate it,' she rejoined. 'So long as it's a kiss on the cheek or the hand.'

'It will be,' he drawled, 'in company.'

She shot a quick look at him, but his profile gave nothing away. It was carved clearly against the desert light, for now they were driving along the road that ploughed through the burning desert. The sands were tawny, like the hide of a great lion, and the road was pitched into mounds and sudden dips by the intensity of the sun. She pondered her childhood days, when sunshine had seemed as lacking as affection, and it filled her with wonderment that the sunshine of this land should be so abundant, so savage almost, flooding down upon the car and warming her right through her dress, a pale sleeveless thing of chiffon, that stopped short of her knees. Her glance took in her legs, long and slim and neatly composed beside the tan slacks of her companion. The sun found the charms on her wrist-chain and set them shining. And when she moved her hand, just a little so he wouldn't notice, the great emerald seemed a pool of mystery.

Words trembled on her lips, and once again her blue eyes were fixed upon his face. Her heart bounded . . . he was a handsome devil! If she had to love someone, and if it had to last her a lifetime, the short time she would be with him, she would not have chosen anyone but this man. Unpredictable, taunting and amused by her unworldliness, he was also the most exciting of men to be with. She liked his eyes, the warmth to his skin when he came too near and she felt compelled to push him away. His shoulders never slouched, and that peak of dark hair was exactly in the centre of his forehead.

Perhaps she was in love with the look of him, never having loved before. But whatever it was, she liked the feeling that she was of use to him. She would do a lot now to please him.

'Did you plan it all along?' The words escaped her. 'I mean, it always seemed a bit beyond reason that I could pass myself off as another girl. Did you intend from the start to introduce me as Janna Smith?'

'Of course,' he admitted shamelessly.

'Then why did you pretend otherwise?'

'I wanted to find out how desperate you were to escape from dull routine. I was curious about you. You were so alone, so untried, so much the orphan that I wondered if you could be faking.'

'That was cruel of you, to think such a thing!'

'Men are a little cruel, *chica*, especially when it comes to someone who mystifies them. I might have been asking a young adventuress to pose as my grandmother's ward. Only a girl of real integrity could have fought the idea as you did. An adventuress would have jumped at the chance. She would have been confident of acting the part. You were frightened, and agreed to my proposition only after your disagreement with Madam Noyes.'

'Knowing I was frightened, you could have told me your real plan.' Bewilderment crept into her eyes; he had played with her like a great cat with a timid mouse, and she wanted to wrench off his ring, but was helpless to do so when he looked at her with those dark eyes that demanded even as they enticed.

'I wanted to give you time to get used to me. Each time I spoke of Joyosa she was there between us, a third person in our lives. But as soon as I told you it was yourself with whom I wished to play the role of a lover I knew you might panic. To be afraid and fighting it is a different thing from panic. I waited until our very last hour in Benikesh to see if you would back out . . . when you didn't I knew the time had come to be completely frank with you.'

'You were so sure I would agree to your real plan, Don Raul?'

'Yes. I knew you would agree out of sheer relief. When I said "be yourself, be Janna Smith," it was as if I had saved you from a quicksand into which you were sinking up to your ears.'

'You devil!' She choked the words. 'No wonder you spoke of enjoying yourself. Oh, how I'd like to pay you back!'

'Being a female I am sure you will find a diabolical way to do so.' A laughter line creased his brown cheek. 'There is a coffee flask in the basket of provisions, and I begin to feel thirsty. Will you pour me a cup, *chica*?'

'Whatever you say, *master*.' She knelt on the seat and reached over to the basket. She opened it, took out one of the flasks and a pair of cups, and resettled in her seat. Then colour burned in her cheeks as she felt his glance on the short chiffon dress that revealed her legs, her arms, and her slim neck. She became acutely aware of his proximity. Little arrows seemed to shoot an exquisite pain through her body. It was as if his glance had caressed her.

She poured him a cup of coffee, which he drank with one hand guiding the wheel of the car. 'Mmmm, delicious,' he murmured.

Janna was acutely aware of everything now, and it was as if he implied something else. She tingled as she sat beside him drinking her own coffee. Whatever would she do if he ever murmured such a word in her ear? Delicious . . . darling . . . desert stars. They were such evocative words, and she was involved with a man who was not exactly a saint.

She shivered . . . half with nerves, half with anticipation of what lay ahead of her. All these sensations were so new to Janna Smith, quiet little orphan, typist and runabout, who had never known the warm joy of nestling close to someone who wanted her.

'It is good coffee,' she said, needing to fill the intimate silence which had fallen between them.

'We have *mocha* coffee trees in El Amara, which are grown

96

along with the tangerines, which have the most magical smell, and various other fruits. Miles of groves. One of the largest in the whole of Morocco. Does it seem strange that the desert should produce fruit on such a scale?'

'Like lots of other people I was inclined to imagine the desert as an arid place.'

'Where there is water running beneath the surface of the desert an oasis will grow of itself, but my grandmother's people have cultivated date palms and fruit trees for over a hundred years. It was started in her father's time, and the Princess hopes it will continue during my lifetime, and my son's.'

'You have a son?' Janna tried to sound casual.

He laughed. 'You evidently think of me as an indulged sheik who has had girls for playthings since I became old enough to appreciate them. No, I have no sons, *chica*. But I hope to have them.'

Rachael's? She who had two small boys already, so lovely, and rather helpless somehow, and so much his concern.

'Do you like tangerines?' he asked.

'Mmm, they remind me of Christmas. We orphans always had one wrapped in silver paper to make it look exciting. A lady in the neighbourhood used to give them to the home.'

'And at my home you will see so many, suspended red-gold and luscious from the trees and filling the air with their fragrance. Crystallised orange flowers, and orange-flower honey are made from them . . . we don't wait for a festive time to enjoy their sweetness.'

She met his eyes and saw a kindness in them, so in contrast to the bold amusement she usually aroused. 'I shan't know myself, *señor*. I shall feel like a kid let loose in a candy shop.'

'You are very unspoiled, Janna. Very young, with much to learn, but much to give in return. Your lover will be a fortunate man, I think.'

'I—I'm not looking for a lover, *señor*.'

'When I speak of a lover, *señorita*, I mean the man who

will become your husband.' His tone became teasing. 'In your country is a husband not a lover?'

'The word has a different meaning,' she said confusedly.

'Extra-marital?' The teasing note deepened.

'Yes, in most cases.'

'Here we regard a man as a lover before anything else. He must be so, to become later on a protector, a father, and a companion. You have nothing to retort, Janna? Do I make you shy with my outspoken remarks? Or does it confuse you to think of being loved by a man?'

'I—I'm not really used to discussing such a subject with a man.'

'Did Madam Noyes talk of such things? Romance is her business.'

'Her ideas of romance weren't exactly mine.'

'What are yours, *señorita*? Or can't you reveal them to a man?'

'They're quite simple.' Her cheeks were warm, and her eyes were fixed upon the desert. 'It must be nice to be the centre of someone's life, to share, and to grow close through the years, so that all the sad, cold things are shut outside when you are together. I would imagine that love—real love—was something like that.'

'You fail to mention excitement, *chica*. The rapture which is also part of real love.'

'I was taking that for granted,' she said demurely.

'That part should never be taken for granted, but being so innocent I suppose you know little about it?'

'I have not had your experience, *señor*.'

'You talk as if I had been a Don Juan. I wonder why?'

'You certainly don't strike me as a choirboy, not with your face.'

'And what is wrong with my face?'

'Not a thing, *señor*. That is half the trouble.'

'Meaning that because I look rather wicked I have behaved so?'

'I expect you've sown quite a few wild oats.'

'It's in the nature of a man, *niña*. And in the nature of a woman to prefer a bit of the devil to a lot of self-righteousness.'

'I know that.' She broke into a smile. 'I'm not an absolute prude, though you keep harping on my innocence. I am twenty years old.'

'Twelve years younger than I, and still quite a child in some ways.'

'Do you suggest that I sow a few wild oats and discard my awful innocence?'

'I regard your innocence as part of your charm . . . there is a pothole in the road ahead, so I won't look your way if you are about to blush.'

They bounced in and out of the dip, and Janna told herself it was the reason her heart turned over, or seemed to. No one had ever told her that she had any charm and though he could be teasing her, she wanted to believe that he meant it. It made life more exciting to be admired by him . . . even as it made this make-believe situation more dangerous.

'If the dazzle of the sun is beginning to make you drowsy, then take a nap,' he suggested. 'I shall drive until the sun is so hot that the wheel and the engine start to bake, then we will find somewhere to park for lunch. Though the desert looks quite barren, there are rock formations which will give us shade until the sun loses some of its ferocity.'

'I never knew the sun could be so brazen.' She looked at Don Raul, who was now wearing smoked glasses, and noticed that his tan shirt was beginning to cling to the firmly muscled shoulders. Noon was approaching, when like a flame the sun would blaze over the sands and set them scorching. It was a frightening prospect, and she was glad the man beside her knew the desert so well and would not break any of the rules that led strangers into trouble. He would ensure that their engine didn't burn out and break down; he would know where they could shelter when the sun reached its zenith.

'Because the days are so warm, the nights are quite cold,'

he said. 'The desert winds start to blow soon after sunset, and at certain times of the year the very dew in the rock pools turns to ice. The desert is a place of strange moods, sudden changes of temperament, and that is why a man never grows tired of it. Like a woman it perpetually challenges and mystifies . . . one moment so warm, the next so cold, like snow off the Atlas peaks themselves.'

'A man's world,' she murmured, 'where a woman might be an intruder.'

'You are having a slight case of nerves,' he said. 'You feel apprehension, a desire and a dislike . . . rather like the feeling a girl might have when for the first time she finds herself alone with a lover.'

It was a most unsettling simile, and yet it described her feelings so exactly. She was eager for what lay ahead of her, and yet at the same time she wanted to return to the safety of an English room, where she could turn the key in the lock and be untouched by the wild forces of life.

'You know altogether too much about female feelings,' she retorted, and resting her head against the shoulder of her seat she closed her eyes against the sun-glare and strove not to think of anything but the motion of the car. She heard him laugh softly . . . it was rather like a purring sound, velvety and resonant, stirring the soft skin at the nape of her slender neck.

'Sleep awhile, *berida*,' he said. 'Rest that active young mind of yours.'

'*Berida?* It isn't a word I've heard before.'

'In Arabic it means girl.'

'It's a nice word, *señor*.'

'Arabic is a poetic language.'

'And you speak it fluently?'

'As fluently as any other desert sheik.' His tone of voice was softly mocking, but she knew he didn't really jest. He was Raul Cesar Bey, and the further they travelled into the desert the more aware she was of his affinity with the savage sun and the tawny sands. Here he was not the worldly traveller whom she had met in the garden of a smart hotel. Here he discarded the suave manners of the cosmopolitan and became the man he really was . . . the grandson of a Moroccan princess. Here his shoulders carried a cloak with inborn grace, his eyes held the dark fires of an imperious nature, his skin the tawny warmth of the desert itself.

On the plane to Casablanca he had asked her if she thought herself the captive of a desert sheik.

She knew in this safari car with him that it was no longer a jest . . . he had made a captive of her heart and bound her to him by a promise. She would be literally his until he was ready to release her from their make-believe involvement. She would not be able to run away. She would at El Amara be a prisoner of his pretended love.

Janna awoke as the car came to a sudden halt. She stirred and thought drowsily that the shoulder of her seat was more comfortable than she had realised. She opened her eyes and found to her surprise that her sun-glasses had been removed and that her head rested upon the warm muscles of a masculine chest. She didn't dare to move for several moments, the aroma of warm male skin in her nostrils, mingling with the tang of tobacco smoke, and the bitter-sweet of healthy perspiration. Such a heady mixture of emotions ran through her . . . a desire to press her face closer against him, to breathe him deep, and never lose him to someone else.

'Awake?' he murmured.

She nodded, and then felt his hand stroking her hair, the lean fingers dwelling on the ruffled softness. 'You sleep so quietly and lightly,' he said. 'Like a lily on a slender stem, as if you might break if unshielded. You are very slight, Janna. I still think you could not have been overfed as a child.'

Her blue eyes looked upward and were held by his dark gaze. Her head was pillowed in the warm hollow of his shoulder. Her heart beat so that he must feel it, and think that it beat in panic at his nearness.

101

'Some people are naturally thin,' she replied.

His hand touched her neck, her shoulder, and very lightly her cheek. 'Small bones, soft skin, a lily or a bird in a man's hand. I can feel your heart like a little wing, beating at my fingers. Does it frighten you to be helpless in my arms, *niña*? If you cried out there would be only the hawks and the rock lizards to hear your pleas.'

'I'm sure my pleas wouldn't move you,' she said, fighting the pull he had on her feelings. 'I'd scratch and bite to my last ounce of strength.'

'I think spirit is the more appropriate word,' he drawled.

'And now shall we have lunch?' She forced herself to speak coolly, but was unable to control the tremor of her lips.

'Food to tame the savage breast—or is it beast?'

'It's taunting devil!' She forced herself out of his arms, grabbed at the door handle and jumped out of the car. For a second, like a gazelle at bay, she looked all around her. Miles of desert sands surrounded them, and above reared a monolith of sandstone rock, casting the shade in which they could lunch, and allow the car engine to cool down.

Don Raul strolled round from the other side of the car, long-legged and lithe, a smile playing at the corner of his lips. 'We will have the cold food which Hussein packed for us and save the chops and eggs for tonight. It is far too warm to light a fire.'

'The eggs would cook of themselves.' Janna retreated into the shade after stepping a moment into the blaze of the sun. 'How awful to be lost and waterless under such a sky!'

'Yes, nature has a cruel side to her, so perhaps we human beings can be forgiven for our lapses from grace.'

'I think you enjoy yours.' She began to unload their picnic gear from the back of the car, and he laughed way above her head as he reached inside for the food hamper.

'My little orphan-angel, I like it when you get into a temper and give me the pepper on your tongue. You enjoy it as well, so don't look at me as if honey wouldn't melt in your mouth.'

'You are enough to infuriate a real angel.' She knelt to lay out the rug, with its Arabian patterns, and upon this she spread the white cloth and the condiments. He opened the hamper and handed her the sealed container of chicken and salad, the loaf with sesame seeds pressed into it, the butter, dates, and the other coffee flask. They ate their food fairly quickly, for there were sandflies about, even in the shadow of the rocks, and after packing away the remains of their lunch they enjoyed with more leisure the delectable coffee which Hussein had prepared for them.

Don Raul stretched out in a patch of shade, lazily alert as a panther, with the same rippling of muscle and dark grace.

'Why don't you get some shut-eye?' Janna suggested. 'I've had mine and will read my book.'

'What is the story?' he asked lazily. 'A romance, no doubt?'

'As it happens, *señor*, the book is a thriller. I had an over-abundance of romance while working for Mildred Noyes.'

'I hope she has not turned you against the real thing?'

'I wouldn't know.' Janna settled down with her shoulders against a boulder. Her eyes were upon the print, but her mind wasn't making much sense of the story. She was too aware of the relaxed male figure who lay nearby, his dark head pillowed upon a car cushion, his eyes half closed. He intruded into everything; her thoughts, her feelings, and even her book. He was altogether too compelling, and she breathed a sigh of relief when his eyelids finally settled into stillness and his face took on the look of sleep.

A smile played about her lips. Even in sleep he didn't return to boyhood. His face remained forceful, striking, with the devil still lurking in his cleft chin.

Romance had played an elusive role in her life, but love had come to her in the shape of a man who was a unpredictable as the desert itself. She gazed at the sands that lay like a golden, becalmed ocean all around this small island of rock. There was not another soul in sight; only a few hawks wheeled lazily in the sky, and she could hear insects scraping their wings in the tamarisk bushes that grew among the rocks. How nervous she would be of this unknown land if Raul Cesar Bey were not at hand to guard and protect her in his sardonic way. The powdered pewter of the sands was polished by the sun, and all the time she could feel herself changing, becoming aware of ardent forces, a limitless freedom to think, feel and enjoy.

No wonder Don Raul returned to the desert with such eagerness. But what of Rachael, with her gentle, civilised beauty, when the time came for him to bring her to El Amara?

Janna couldn't imagine Rachael enjoying an alfresco lunch in the desert, bumping over the sands in a safari car, or sleeping under the stars. She seemed a woman who liked her creature comforts . . . had not Don Raul persuaded the Princess Yamila to provide Rachael with an income which enabled her to live in comfort?

It was a perplexing situation, but Janna didn't doubt that Don Raul would work it out to his satisfaction. He was not a man to let anything stand in the way of something he really wanted . . . and Janna was to be used to prove to the Princess that only the young widow could ever make him happy. He wanted a woman of the world, not a naïve girl who moved him to amusement rather than ardency.

CHAPTER EIGHT

THE print of her book danced in front of Janna's eyes and she gave up trying to read and let a warm lethargy steal over her. She was half dreaming when something touched her leg, crawled on to her dress and brought her awake in a second. She stared in horror at the black, crook-legged thing that crouched on the pale chiffon of her skirt. She had never seen an insect so large, and with an uncontrollable scream she leapt to her feet and brushed it away madly.

Don Raul was awake and on his feet in an instant. 'What was it?' he demanded.

'A—a scorpion . . . big and black!'

He frowned at her, and then his eyes flashed to the ground in time to see the large insect scuttle away into the cover of some dried grass. There it made a creaking sound, and Janna gazed in hurt amazement as Don Raul gave a chuckle.

'It was a cricket . . . here in the desert they grow larger than elsewhere.'

She swallowed dryly. 'There's no need to laugh! It looked horrible to me, so black and leggy. I thought crickets were small and pale, like match-toys.'

'If it had been a black scorpion and you had disturbed it in that way, it might have stung you. Always remain very still and don't move until it crawls off your person.'

'That's easy to say.' She put a shaky hand to her throat. 'You're used to the insects that live in the desert, but I'm a stranger to them.'

'You are also a female,' he drawled. 'I understand your fear of what is ugly, but if ever a scorpion comes anywhere near you, try not to get into a panic. The sting of the black species is deadly; the other sort may give you a fever.'

'Men always take a superior attitude when it comes to the things that women fear. Is there nothing that frightens you?'

He stood and considered her question, his hands in the pockets of his slacks, his eyes searching her face with a lazy interest. 'I think I would be afraid of losing something I really wanted. To do so might turn me to the devil . . . though I believe you think me a close connection of his already.'

'You seem to get a kick out of my inexperience, which is rather unkind.'

'I think it better to laugh at some of your antics than to

baby them. This desert is a place to face up to, and once your nervousness wears off you will begin to be fascinated, and in a while to grow fond of it. It is like going to a dance for the first time, you must stumble before you fall into the rhythm. You must taste the bitter before the sweet. That is a fact of life.'

'I certainly don't wish to be babied, *señor*. But you aren't the most sympathetic person I've ever met.'

'If I were sympathetic you would be alarmed. I think you and I are inclined to forget that we are virtual strangers to each other. I have much to learn about you, you have a lot to learn about me. We can't expect to fall into step without a few stumbles, eh?'

She shook her head, and wondered if he would talk this way if Rachael were with him and a fat black cricket had crawled up her leg.

The sun still burned in the sky and the hush of breathless heat lay over the day, but with sudden decision Don Raul began to collect together the hamper, cushions and rug. 'We will make a move,' he said. 'Soon it will be mid-afternoon, when the heat begins to abate. We have a good five hours' driving ahead of us before we need make camp for the night.'

'I submit with never a murmur, *señor*.'

He cast a look at her as she followed him to the car, an eyebrow quirked. 'I wonder what you hide behind that demure reply? What are you thinking as you look at me with such innocent eyes? It really is the truth, that a worldly woman is a mirror which reflects all that she is. You, *niña*, are like a pool that hides things beneath a limpid surface.'

'You make me sound secretive, *señor*. What have I to hide?'

'I wonder,' he murmured.

Several minutes later they were driving away from the rocks, leaving only their footmarks in the sand. Yet Janna would not forget the place; it was there he had talked of turning to the devil if deprived of what he really wanted.

She stole a glance at his profile. He was unaware that she loved him, and it was something he must be kept from learning. Whenever he touched her, she must betray no response to him. She must fight him at every turn and keep her pride, at least. To be betrayed by her own self would be mortifying. She was the girl hired to wear his ring. She was briefly required to amuse the Princess . . . love didn't enter into the bargain.

It was about an hour later when vivid streamers of rose-gold began to appear in the sky. In stealth, almost, velvety shadows began to steal over the sands, and Janna felt a welcome coolness blowing in through the open windows of the car. The next few miles of their journey took on the pleasure of driving without puffs of heat coming in from the engine and the desert. She breathed the tangy air and it was as if the pores of the earth had opened to give off a strange wild fragrance as dusk began to fall.

'Soon you will see why I regard the desert as a place of beauty,' said Don Raul. 'Why the senses respond to its magic and forget how relentless it can be.'

Already she could feel a magic stealing over the day. And then came a sound that added witchery, a hint of the pagan, a throb that was echoed by Janna's heart. Quite suddenly the car came in sight of a straggling stone village nestling at the foot of a range of hills. The sound was that of a flute as a boy stood piping sheep down the hillside. Don Raul stopped driving and they watched as the short-legged bales of wool tumbled and bleated and milled about the car.

Flames leapt in the shadow of primitive houses and women in long dresses prepared meals over the tamarisk fires. Children ran about. Dogs barked. A drum pounded. The shepherd and his flock went on their way down a lane that twisted between the mud-brick dwellings.

They drove on and Janna was aware of dark eyes watching them from beneath the cowls of bygone clothing. It was as if for a few minutes they had driven into the past and seen people who lived as in the days of Naomi and Ruth.

'Things change slowly in the desert,' said Don Raul. 'Life here is like the palm tree, its roots lost in the past, its appearance always the same. In the desert we don't question the mystery of dusk and dawn, of life and love. These are part of the drama of living. The crests and the depths, like the sands themselves. In cities time hurries by, friends are found and lost, values are less profound. In cities a man admires the ability to pile up possessions; here it is good to have the things that don't crowd the tent; a splendid carpet, a copper lamp, and a pair of lustrous eyes.'

His words moved Janna. She had thought him a man of the world, seeking pleasure and careless of tomorrow. She had been so mistaken. Love of desert places and people ran in his veins, and here he was far more disturbing than he had been the evening they had eaten flaming plums together.

He looked at her and the brilliant darkness of his gaze held her at his mercy. 'You are beginning to feel the magic,' he said. 'I can see it in your eyes.'

At once she was alarmed. He might see in her eyes more than she wished to reveal, and she looked away forcibly and gave herself up to the almost savage beauty of the desert sunset. A fantastic tangling of colours, a web holding the sun as it blazed immense and golden in the deepening sky. Was it from this palette that the rainbow drew its lovely arc? Were the silk dyers inspired by such a riot of tones and shades? Was it real or a mirage, the sheer beauty of rose-gold, palest green and violet, against which a cluster of desert palm trees bowed, the sunset flames burning the edges of the long notched leaves that cloaked their slenderness?

'It's more than beautiful,' Janna murmured. 'It's so alive, and yet the sun is dying.'

'You will see that savage loneliness with each passing of the sun, and you will always see it with wonder.'

'But this is my first sunset in the desert, señor. Those trees, that rocky village, the singing winds, these are the essence of my memory.'

'You are unusual, *niña*. Many women place jewels before the splendour of a sunset, or the glow of a star.'

'I am not sophisticated. Even your emerald seems false to me beside such beauty.'

'You don't much like my emerald, do you?'

'It feels out of place on my hand.'

'Up on the *muezzin* tower last night you reached out as if for a star. The gesture was significant.'

'You seem to place a symbolic meaning upon everything, *señor*.'

'You were reaching for something, *niña*.'

'It would not be surprising. The orphan's dream seems always out of reach.'

'Always is a long, long time.'

'I suppose so. It used to seem a wonderful dream to me that lots of people had a family fire to cluster around when winter came, with a dog romping through rooms where books and cushions were scattered about, and where muffins were toasted and someone played the piano.'

'All of us are the victims of certain dreams. Can you guess mine?'

She thought of Rachael, of the palm and pomegranate groves of his home, and of the son he must have. His dreams were more easily fulfilled than her own, but the two boys born already to the woman he wanted would make doubly hard his task of proving to the Princess that a young, unworldly girl was not for him. How would he set about proving it? Would he be unkind and hurtful . . . to herself?

Dusk drew its great paw over the sands and they slowly darkened; the evening winds sang across them.

'You have not yet answered my question, Janna.'

She gave him a cautious look. 'I wouldn't presume to guess your dreams, Don Raul. You might laugh at my nonsense.'

'You have not let that deter you before. Come, do I dream of happiness and love?'

'You . . . are loved.'

'By whom, do you suppose?'

She flushed in the darkness. 'By your grandmother, and the people at El Amara. By——'

'Yes, by whom else?'

'Your cousin.'

'I have several.'

'Don Raul,' she forced a laugh, 'I don't know what I've done to deserve this inquisition. Are you practising?'

'Practising what, *niña*?'

'A little Spanish torment.'

'Why should I wish to torment you?'

'You have to show the Princess what a failure a mere girl would be as your wife.'

'And you think I shall use thumb-screws on you?' He laughed, a soft mocking sound. 'You have a vivid imagination, and it can distort facts and fancies, turn a carefree remark into a certainty, a fiction into a truth.'

'Are you telling me to control my imagination?'

'You are a little inclined to let it run away with you.'

'You were the one who mentioned thumb-screws!'

'You child,' he mocked. 'What a lot you have to learn!'

'I daresay I have, but I'm not asking you to be my teacher.'

'Afraid, *chica*?'

She refused to be drawn further into a dangerous discussion. 'Look, the stars are coming out. So many, like shoals of silver fish.'

'It will now begin to grow colder. Shut the window beside you and put on your jacket. We will drive for a few more miles.'

She did as he told her, and was really amazed to feel how chilly it had grown after the intense heat of the day. She knelt on the seat and searched for her jacket, until she remembered that it was locked in her suitcase.

'Wear mine,' he said firmly. 'You should find it beside the torch and the medical kit.'

'Don't you want it yourself?'

'Not just yet. I'm not wearing such flimsy clothing as yourself. Put it on before you start shivering.'

She did so, and couldn't suppress a laugh. She was lost in the largeness of it and could feel the silky lining against her arms and the weight of his cigarette case and lighter in the pocket.

'Would you like to smoke?' she asked.

'Very much. Light one for me, *niña*. I don't want to take my hands off the wheel. Despite all those stars this desert road is a dark one and I don't want to run into a clump of rocks or an animal.'

Janna opened the flat gold case, took out one of the cigarettes and put the filter between her lips. She spun the lighter and lit up, and suddenly that shattering sense of intimacy was back between them. She wore his jacket, he took between his lips the cigarette her lips had touched.

'*Gracias.*'

'It's a nice word.' She fought to sound casual.

'Ours is a gracious language. You must allow me to teach you how to speak it.'

'Shall I be at El Amara long enough to learn it?'

'Some Spanish and a little Arabic should make you an unusual tea-shop proprietress,' he drawled. 'The good ladies of the seaside resort will flock in for tea and cakes just to hear all about your captivity by a sheik of the desert. You will make a small fortune.'

'As if I'd advertise it!' she said indignantly. 'What do you take me for?'

'I have heard that the romantic ladies of small unexciting towns are partial to the belief that southern men have a passion for the fair-haired girls of the cool north.'

'I know differently, *señor.*'

'You mean the good ladies would not like you to be involved with someone like me?'

'I mean it just isn't true, is it, that southern men are attracted to fair-haired girls. You felt no love for Joyosa.'

'She left me cold, *chica.*'

111

'Which goes to prove that you respond to dark hair and eyes. I think it's natural for everyone to like those who look and behave like their parents.'

'Which places you in quite a dilemma, my child.'

Janna was lost for a reply, and saved from one, for in that instant there was a bump and a squeal as the car ran into some object on the dark and lonely road. They came to a jolting halt, and Don Raul muttered a less gracious Spanish word. 'I have hit something!'

'Well, don't look at me as if I'm to blame,' she said. 'I'd be quite content to sit and not talk while you drive.'

'Come, let us take a look!'

He swung open the door on his side, reached for the torch and was soon peering under the car to see what they had hit. Janna gave a shocked gasp and backed away from what the torchlight revealed—a jackal, quite dead, and with a smaller animal clamped between its jaws.

'A jerboa.' Don Raul turned to Janna, who stood shivering slightly in his jacket, which reached to her hips and made her look rather helpless.

'I am going to back the car,' he said. 'Step to the roadside and don't look if you are squeamish.'

'The poor thing,' she said shakily.

'A jackal preys on whatever it can. A group of them will attack a lonely traveller. It isn't a jolly romping dog, so don't be foolish.'

Tears started to her eyes and she stepped off the road and turned her back on him. She heard the car start up, heard the wheels lurch, and hunched down in his jacket as he drove around the released object and came to a halt beside her.

She climbed in without saying a word and they drove on. 'We will make camp very soon,' he said. 'You are hungry, tired, and hating me.'

'You have no feelings.'

'I have them, *chica*, but not to waste on jackals, or on foolish sulks.'

'I don't want to disturb your driving, so I'll sit quiet. You might run into a camel next time.'

'Sit as quiet as you please,' he chuckled. 'I have plenty to occupy my mind . . . and by the way, Arabs call their women little camels when they are being obstinate.'

'I—I don't like heartless people.'

'I am merely a hungry man who has been driving for a long while and is beginning to feel the strain. Have you no heart, *chica*?'

At once she felt contrite. The road ahead was dark, and their headlamp on the left side seemed to be dimming. It must have taken a crack when they had hit the jackal . . . which had been on the prey and had killed one of those furry large-eyed jerboas with a snap of its jaws. It was silly of her to act the outraged female with Don Raul, but she hated to see a spider stamped on.

'I am sorry if I appear callous to you,' he said, 'but I would have been truly regretful if the animal had been a gazelle or a hare.'

'Don't you hunt gazelle?' she asked.

'It has now been forbidden and those graceful, dappled creatures run free. You should be pleased about that, though I admit to hunting wild boar, or the occasional forest panther. Despite all this desert, there are regions where we have cedar forests in which the killer cat roams.'

'I'm certainly glad the gazelle is left in peace,' she murmured.

'You dislike the hunt, eh? Yet love has been likened to the hunting game.'

'There is no cruelty at the end of the . . . chase.'

'There is often unwilling surrender, and that is why I dislike the arranged marriage. Sometimes a couple adjust to the arrangement, but excitement and ardency are missing from their relationship . . . the thrill of looking at someone and knowing you would give up everything to be with that person all your life.'

In the flicker of the overhead light Janna looked at him

and saw a serious profile. He meant every word! As much as El Amara meant to him, and despite his affection for the Princess, he would be prepared to give it all up . . . for the sake of the woman he loved.

All at once the car slowed down and he peered out of the window along the beam of the headlamps. 'I can see some palm trees and a patch of scrub or tamarisk. We will stop here for the night and make a large fire, boil a pot of coffee, cook our supper, and bed down under the stars.'

He swung the safari car off the road and they bumped over the sand towards the group of trees, and the bushes that would provide fuel for their fire.

Janna felt a sense of relief that at last they were stopping, and also a quickening of her pulses. Here she would be entirely alone for the night with a man she was entirely unsure of, a man who could be shatteringly kind and also a little cruel. A man who thrilled her and made everything seem more exciting.

The inscrutable desert lay all around them, and their tamarisk fire scented the air. Groups of stars curved like comets across the indigo velvet of the sky. Everything was disturbing in a most subtle way . . . the mingled aromas of smoke and meat, the rustle of the palms, the tall figure who held the frying pan so the chops didn't burn.

Janna still wore his jacket, while he had slung about him with careless ease a *burnous* of long classic folds, so that in the firelight he looked more than ever a man of the desert.

'The chops are sizzling,' he said. 'If you will break the eggs in that dish and beat them, I will make an omelette.'

'You are very self-sufficient, Don Raul.' She broke the eggs and beat them with a fork. 'I thought the grandson of a Princess would be more used to being waited upon.'

'I was not reared in a pasha environment,' he drawled. 'My grandmother saw to it that I was never pampered, and during my youth I attended one of the toughest schools in

114

England, and I have also served in the Royal Moroccan Army. Did you imagine that I had *houris* waiting upon me day and night?'

She looked at him and saw the shadows of fire flickering over the lean strength of his face. His wide shoulders carried the *burnous* with the grace of a man who was supple in the saddle and totally unspoiled by a soft life.

'Not really,' she smiled. 'Did you enjoy being a soldier?'

'Each experience is of importance and adds to one's knowledge of life. I found the British people very interesting. I liked their tolerance, their casual humour, their strange cool courage, and their distinction.'

'You flatter us, *señor*.'

'Not at all. I never pay a compliment unless I mean it, and that was something I learned also from your people.'

'You learned excellent English. I could never hope to speak such good Spanish.'

'You will surprise yourself, *señorita*.' He took from her the beaten eggs and tipped them into the pan, where in a moment the omelette began to bubble. The chops lay in a container at the edge of the fire to keep warm, and the air was redolent of the good smell of well-cooked food. Janna could feel her appetite stirring as she sliced bread and laid out the plates and cutlery. It was an exciting new experience for her, to be camping like this beside a tamarisk fire in the heart of the Moroccan desert.

Amazing that only a week ago she had been boxed up in a hotel room, her future in the hands of Mildred Noyes. By a strange stroke of fate she was now experiencing the joy and terror of being entirely in the hands of Raul Cesar Bey.

It amused him to refer to himself as a sheik of the desert, but it was not far from the truth. With the cool audacity of one he had carried her away with him ... and she didn't dare to guess his thoughts as she met his gaze in the fire-light and saw that slightly wicked smile at the edge of his bold mouth.

'Hungry?' he asked.

She nodded. 'The food smells appetising.'

'Hold out your plate.' She did so and half the omelette was placed upon it, golden and fluffy. Next came one of the crisp lamb chops and gravy. 'Now you may tuck in.'

'*Gracias.*' She smiled shyly to be using that lovely Spanish word for thanks.

'*De nada, niña.*' He sat down on the soft sandy ground beside her. 'Which means you are welcome.'

'Mmm, delicious.' She had never eaten anything more tasty than this meal enjoyed beside a fire of crackling branches, with overhead the rustling murmur of palm leaves, and seen through their fronds the jewelled night sky.

'What are you thinking?' Don Raul had taken the edge off his appetite and was giving her a quizzical look. 'That all this is very different from life with Madam Noyes?'

'It couldn't be more different,' she replied, a catch of amusement and wonder in her voice. 'I'm inclined to wonder if I'm dreaming.'

'If you are, *niña,* then it is quite a pleasant dream, eh?'

'I can't deny it, *señor.*' She accepted another cup of Arabian coffee, to which broken sugar was added. It had a rich aroma, a heavenly taste.

'Yesterday you were reserved, tonight you smile. You feel the call of the desert, and there is no other quite so subtle, so filled with a sense of destiny. Look!' He indicated the sky and together they watched as a star fell through the darkness like a silver arrow. 'Destiny weaves the pattern of one's life, and here in the desert at night one is more aware of this than elsewhere. The doors of the heart seem to open to let in the secret of happiness ... which is simplicity, the singing harps of silence in tune with the stars.'

'You speak like a poet, *señor.*'

'I have in my veins the voice of Andalucia and Arabia.' He held her eyes with his, and she was intensely aware of their depth and magnetism. 'My grandmother is pure Berber and her skin is as milk-white as your own, but the

116

word Berber springs from barbarian ... did you know that?'

'No, but I can believe it,' she half smiled, disturbed by his nearness in the black folds of his *burnous*, and by his gaze upon her face and her throat in the opening of his jacket.

'I make you feel shy?'

'I—I'm never sure of what you are thinking.'

'Right now that your fair colouring and your blue eyes make you seem as if dipped in well water, so that a cool freshness clings to you.'

Her cheeks weren't cool as he spoke, and she sought wildly for a less personal topic of conversation. 'Tell me more about your grandmother! She sounds so fascinating.'

'One of the two most intriguing women I have ever met.' He lounged at his ease on one elbow, enjoying the warmth of the fire like a great cat lazily replete after a good meal. 'She has known colourful, stormy times, and the tragedy of losing her two sons, one of them to the war in Spain, the other at sea ... my own father. She has always been a great beauty, and like most women she purrs when she gets her own way, and can be terrible if fate works in opposition to her plans. She has the vital will of the frail. A man likes to give in to her, but it isn't always wise to do so. I gave in with regard to Joyosa, knowing in my heart that we were not suited. Now the Princess must give in to me, and it will be a tussle.'

'With me in the middle,' Janna nervously smiled, 'being pulled two ways.'

'She may be delighted with you,' he drawled.

'Which will make things more awkward than ever for you, *señor*.' Janna's eyes widened, deep blue and startled in the firelight. 'She may expect you ... to marry me.'

'She may indeed, *niña*.'

'Whatever will you do? Don Raul, a while ago you talked of being with the woman you loved ... if it meant giving up your heritage!'

117

'To be with her—whom I love—would be worth any sacrifice. I am a Latin by birth and therefore when I take a wife, I take her for always. For the *bedouin* life is simpler. He can marry on Monday and divorce on Friday if the woman displeases him. He is not compelled by Moslem law to stay bound to a woman who is miles apart from him in temperament; in everything that can make a marriage an exciting love affair.'

'It is all very perplexing——'

'Poor child.' He took her slim, tense hand in his and fingered the emerald ring. 'So much has happened in just a few days and your mind is spinning. For tonight don't let us talk any more of what lies ahead of you at El Amara. Let Kismet carry you along, for it will regardless of your struggles. It will decide the outcome of what seems so perplexing right now.'

'You mean we must let things take their course? But supposing—'

'Don't worry, *chica*.' That slightly mocking note came into his voice. 'I know you think of the desert as a place where men enforce their will regardless of a girl's wishes, but most of that takes place only in the novels of Madam Noyes. I promise you that whenever you wish to leave El Amara you will be free to go.'

'No matter what the Princess decrees?'

'The Princess is not in charge of your destiny, Janna.'

'Are you, Don Raul?'

'In that I take you to my home at El Amara. But you may return my ring and return to England whenever you want to.'

'I thought the decision would be yours, *señor*.'

'Not entirely. A month at the oasis may be more than enough for you, so I am not being the tyrant with regard to how long you stay with my family. You may grow to like us.'

'And if I do?' She awaited his answer with a tenseness she tried not to reveal, jingling the little charms on her

118

wrist chain, golden trifles that caught the firelight ... and the glance of his dark eyes.

'An English tea-shop should be quite a novelty in the *souk* of El Amara,' he said casually. 'You could stay and open one there.'

'I suppose I could.' She tried to sound as casual as he, as if she hadn't hoped for a warmer reply. She was a little fool. As if he really cared what she did in the future ... he was only concerned for Rachael and his grandmother. She was to be the bridge that brought them together. The English girl he would discard when he had convinced the autocratic Princess that he could be happy with no one but the woman of his choice ...

'I shall have to think about it, *señor*.'

'You mean the tea-shop in the *souk*?'

She smiled. 'I can just see myself serving tea to robed Arabians, clad in a frilly apron and a severe dark dress!'

'A most attractive picture,' he drawled. 'I shall have to come and sample your tea and cakes. Right now you may pour me another cup of coffee, and I would also relish one of those figs.'

She found a plump one, and with a grin that concealed her true feelings she put it to his lips. He opened them and the white, straight line of his teeth closed upon the sweet morsel. All the time he looked at her, his eyes as dark and unfathomable as the desert all around them.

CHAPTER NINE

SILENCE fell between them, and Janna glanced into the surrounding shadows of the desert. Strange vibrations seemed to pulse in the night air, there was a feeling of timelessness, a wild fragrance on the wind. It was a silence broken now and then by a distant yelping, as of jackals on the prowl, and by the tamarisk fire breaking into flame and sending a shaft of scented smoke and sparks into the air.

The night was full of mystery, of a breathtaking freedom, of an ardency as pure as the stars themselves, way up there and yet giving the illusion of being within reach of one's fingertips.

Don Raul had likened the desert to a woman, and indeed it had the allure of a woman veiled in chiffon and adorned with jewels. 'How peaceful,' Janna murmured. 'Yet one senses something primitive, a closeness to the heart of things.'

'It makes a city night seem artificial, eh? The neons, the tall buildings, the couples seeking solace in a dimly lit *bistro* where jazz music drifts from a radio. Man has fashioned a civilisation and made himself discontented.'

'Yet everyone talks of the need for progress,' she said.

'A progress that turns upon itself like a snake and stings its own tail.'

'I can understand why you return so eagerly to the desert, *señor*.'

'Here one can breathe and hear the silence. There is no din of traffic, no crash of a building falling and another arising in its place.'

'Perhaps we are old-fashioned people, *señor*.'

'I know that I prefer the freedom of the desert, but the novelty may wear off for you. You are very young, and rather insecure, and in cities people dash past each other, afraid of friendship because it means becoming involved in the hopes and cares of someone else. You are like a kitten among tigers, Janna Smith.'

'A kitten who has become involved with a tiger,' she smiled.

He laughed and it was like a purr deep in his throat. 'Perhaps so, but like a kitten you have a certain shy audacity. Have you noticed how one will climb to a high branch out of curiosity?'

'Meaning?'

'That you dared to come this far with a man like me.'

'What kind of a man are you ... really?'

'Are you enquiring into my love life?'

'No—as if I'd do such a thing!'

'You are,' he said wickedly. 'You believe I have a *harem* tucked away in the house of the pomegranate. Come, admit your fear.'

'Why should I be in fear?'

'If I have a *harem*, then you may think yourself in danger of becoming a member of it.'

She held her breath and her eyes were fixed upon his face in a half-frightened way. Then he laughed and she could have slapped him for making her almost believe the absurdity. 'You enjoy playing on my naïveté, don't you?' Her cheeks burned. 'Still, anything is possible with a man so unconventional.'

'I don't happen to think you a conventional girl. In fact you are most unusual.'

'It must be a bit novel for you to meet a girl of my age who has never been involved in a romance.'

'A dangerous state of affairs,' he drawled. 'You might be ripe to fall in love out of curiosity, and I have a handsome young cousin at El Amara—Ahmed, a name which means "praiseworthy one" in Arabic.'

'Do you think girls like a handsome face?'

'It sometimes blinds them to other qualities.'

She didn't dare to look at Don Raul's face in the dancing light of the fire; already she loved each feature and every expression, even the look of deep amusement that came into his eyes when she voiced her youthful opinion on a subject, or dared to argue with him, a man of the world.

'I—I can't pretend to know much about men, *señor*. I admire interesting faces, but I know that men are attracted to the beautiful face rather than the ordinary one.'

'Angling for a compliment, Janna?'

'No.' She gave him an indignant look. 'I prefer the truth to a flattery, and I wouldn't want to be told something ridiculously untrue. I'm quite ordinary ... but I thought Doña Rachael had a lovely face. She reminded me of a Madonna.'

'You remind me of several things.'

'Kittens and twigs?'

'Periwinkles and water-gardens, and mimosa against a pale wall. You are not in any sense a classic beauty, but nor are you a girl to go unnoticed by the male eye. You have, however, an air of retreat, and Madam Noyes took such advantage of it that you were quite eclipsed—until I saw you in the mimosa. You might then have gone unnoticed but for the immensity of your eyes and how blue they are when you are startled. What was it about me that made you look like a doe caught in a thicket?'

'You must know the answer to that one yourself, Don Raul.'

'Indeed? My wicked looks?'

'Partly.'

'And what else? Come, I insist on being told.'

'The fact that I saw you say something to Doña Rachael that made her cry.'

'Ah—shall I tell you what I said to her?'

'No——'

'I told her that she was not going to suffer for her foolish sister's sake. That I would ensure that the Princess Yamila did not visit her anger upon the rest of Joyosa's family.'

'Then ... her tears were not because you had hurt her?'

'On the contrary.'

'Of course.' Janna's voice softened. 'You couldn't hurt anyone so lovely.'

'No. It would be like taking a flimsy-winged moth in hand and crushing it.'

'I—I'm sorry I misjudged you, *señor*.'

'You judge from this face of mine,' he said quizzically.

Yes, she thought. He was as handsome as Lucifer, but behind his devilish smile he could also be so kind that he made a woman weep. And she—foolish and naïve—had

122

thought those tears of Rachael's caused by unkind words from him!

'I've never met a person quite like you, *señor*. There is a baffling side to you, as if you almost enjoy being thought a shade more devilish than you really are.'

'It comes as a relief that I don't bite after all?' In one swift movement he carried her hand to his lips. 'Not to the bone, that is.'

'Please——' She tried to pull her hand away, but instead it was pressed close to his lips so that she felt them move in a smile.

'You talk so bravely, eh? Inwardly you are terrified of me and my intentions. Poor child, you would prefer to be with a grey-eyed earnest young man who would talk of everything but men and women and the battle of love.'

'I—I'm very tired,' Janna said desperately. 'Can't we go to bed now?'

'By all means,' he said softly, the firelight revealing the deep wicked smile in his eyes, 'if you wish to.'

'Don Raul!' She jumped to her feet, jerking her hand from his fingers, and almost on the verge of dashing off as if there were a young women's hostel around the corner of the palm trees. 'Y-you know I'm not used to being alone like this with a man and you seem to take advantage of the fact.'

He just looked at her, and then with a single lithe movement he was on his feet and his *burnous* folded dark around his tall figure. He towered over her, making her more aware than ever of his unpredictable maleness, and her own helpless aloneness with him. It wasn't fair that he should have her so at the mercy of his dangerous charm. It wasn't fair of him to behave like this because they were alone, and he wished he had Rachael with him.

'You can't know the meaning of being taken advantage of,' he said cuttingly. 'Have I made advances to you? Have I shown the slightest sign that I am panting to make love to you? I am flattered that I have only to touch your hand

and you imagine yourself in danger!'

Her cheeks stung; he made her seem the one who was panting for love, and she knew too late that if she had kept cool he would not have done more than tease her. Now he was looking at her with a searching glint in his eyes, as if he had begun to suspect that his touch did more than alarm her.

Her heart beat quickly as she awaited the next move from him. She couldn't speak ... her voice would shake, the tears of youthful blunder and bewilderment might choke her. There was nothing more tormenting than to fall in love with a man from whom you had to hide your feelings ... for the sake of pride, and because he loved already someone lovely. She was just a naïve girl who amused him.

'Your eyes look as if they are aching for sleep.' When he turned away from her and strode to the safari car she swayed from the reaction of those few tense moments.

She watched, hands clenched in the pockets of his jacket, as he took the sleeping bags from the car and carried them to the fireside. He unrolled them and pulled down the zippers. The soft quilted linings were revealed, warm-looking, and needed, for the wind across the desert carried a chill that made Janna shiver as it blew against her face and neck.

'Come, we will sleep at this side side of the fire and the trees will shelter us.'

Her eyes, the servants of her emotions, dared not meet his gaze as she walked to the sleeping-bag he indicated. She took off his jacket and her shoes and slipped into the quilted bag. He knelt and zipped it into place around her, snug, comfortable, making her feel disarmed and yet secure.

'Thank you,' she murmured.

'Demure and provoking, aren't you?' He studied her hair, a ruffle of pale gold about her features with their give-away look of youthful uncertainty. Her mouth was soft, questioning.

'Are you afraid that because you wear my ring I shall forget that you are only pretending to be my sweetheart?'

'It is all pretence,' she said, while her heart beneath the quilt and the light touch of his hand cried a different cry.

'Yes, just a game, *chica*.' His smile was a quirk of the lip, but his eyes were serious, as if warning her that in future she was not to take seriously whatever he might do or say. 'Is tonight the first time you have slept beneath the stars?'

'Yes. How close they seem, how warmly they glow, like so many eyes looking down at us.'

'The eyes of guardian angels?'

She broke into a smile. 'Perhaps, *señor*.'

'Then you may sleep safe through the night ... even though I shall be within touching distance.'

'I'm glad——' She bit her lip. 'I mean—I should be nervous of all this surrounding desert, and the jackals, if you weren't nearby.'

'They won't come close to our fire, and I have the habit of sleeping on the alert.' A smile drew a line down his cheek. 'You look like a child ... your feet don't reach to the bottom of the sleeping bag!'

He was touching her feet as he spoke and she gave a nervous laugh. 'Don't—I'm ticklish!'

'So young,' he mused, 'with so much yet to learn. You make me remember the first time I slept out in the desert, and how vast everything seemed to me. I was a mere boy of nine and nothing had ever seemed more exciting to me, or so awesome. I understand your feelings, *chica*.'

He didn't understand them fully, and she smiled a little. She was not a young boy of nine but a girl of twenty, far from all that was familiar to her, and alone in the desert, under the stars, with a man she loved. He couldn't begin to guess how madly her heart beat when he touched her face very lightly with his lean fingers, tracing with a fingertip the line of her cheek to her lips.

'Are you glad you came?' he asked.

'I wouldn't have missed the trip, *señor*.'

'Tomorrow we shall arrive at El Amara and your ordeal will really begin.'

'I—I still wonder if it wouldn't be best for you to tell the Princess the complete truth.'

'And how would I explain you to her?' he drawled.

'I—don't know.'

'Nor do I, and as she is expecting me to arrive with a sweetheart I think it best I arrive with one. I don't wish her to be disappointed, annoyed, and concerned for my future. According to custom I should be married by now, with young children for her to spoil. It will soften the blow for her if she believes I have taken the trouble to find someone as young and fair as Joyosa, but with more character.'

'I—I'm not going to enjoy deceiving her.'

'Don't think of it as a deception.'

'But it is one!'

'Which should make things easier for you. You know you are not really doomed to become my bride.'

He rose to his feet and the dark *burnous* gave him a dramatic look as he turned away and went to the fire, where he threw on more of the branches that burned with such an evocative scent. He loomed tall against the dancing firelight, the sparks bursting in the air about him, his words like painful little blows that Janna had to bear in silence, until she fell asleep.

Janna opened her eyes and stretched. Where on earth was she? She tried to sit up and realised that she was zipped into a sleeping bag. She wriggled until she reached the zip and a moment later was on her feet and looking at her first desert dawn.

Everything was amber and still, and immensely disturbing. The trees were like jade carvings, as if nothing came to life until the sun arose and touched the amber scrolls of sand to warmth, and the long palm leaves to a living green. There upon a boulder lay a chameleon with a jewelled back and eyes of stone. When Janna turned her head she saw

126

Don Raul stretched motionless in his sleeping-bag, his face so still that she felt the quickening of her heartbeats.

It was as if an enchantment lay over the desert, leaving her the onlooker, with eyes that couldn't look away from that sleeping face, the dark hair ruffled on the broad brow, the lashes thick along the curve of the eyelids, the nose autocratic even in slumber, the lips a little open, as if they faintly smiled, the cleft in the chin holding a shadow.

She sighed and would have liked to kneel and kiss that faint smile on his mouth. It was strange that one could feel so shaken and moved, so protective and helpless, so ardent and shy and incredibly adoring all at the same time ... and all this for a man who felt none of it for her.

She turned away resolutely and went to the car to collect her toilet bag and to get a change of clothing out of her suitcase. She went among the palm trees, where she washed herself with the water he had set aside for this purpose. She stood her mirror in the fork of a tree and combed her hair into a bright cloud about her temples and nape. In her white blouse with a blue polka-dot tie, and a white skirt with pleated panels, she had an idea she looked rather like a schoolgirl. Very cool and English and unsuitable for the suave, experienced grandson of a Princess.

She glanced at her hand, at the huge emerald glimmering without flaw, to which was attached the legend of a tragic love. Now the ring was being used to deceive, and Janna felt for a moment as if something touched her in warning, but when she turned to look it was only a pendent palm leaf that brushed her shoulder.

She hastened from the grove and collided directly with Don Raul. His hands closed upon her waist and she was held immobile.

'You must have been awake very early,' he said. 'How pristine you look! You make me feel very unshaved.'

'You do look rather raffish.' She smiled up at him nervously. 'Shall I prepare breakfast while you have a wash and a shave?'

'That would be nice. It's in the nature of the brute to enjoy being waited upon by someone as fresh as new milk.' As he spoke he seemed to breathe more quickly, and Janna found him closer to her, so warm and alive, so attractive despite the dark shadowing of his beard. Her blue eyes seemed to fill with him, her lips parted on a lost breath, and then she felt his kiss in the tiny hollow under her cheek-bone.

'Y-your beard scratches,' she said, turning her head blindly to avoid his lips on hers. He mustn't kiss her properly. She would give herself away to him if he did that.

'My apologies, *niña*. That is the trouble with being a man —neither his beard nor his inclinations are easily con-trolled. You on the other hand are such a cool young thing and I wonder what it would take to shatter your composure so completely that you would beg a kiss rather than resist one. What would it take, little piece of snow?'

'Snow, in the desert?' she scoffed.

'You look it, and you feel it.' His eyes raked her cool skin, her white dress, her pale gold hair. These were her allies. They made her look the composed young miss he thought her.

'Please let me go, *señor*.'

'Afraid my touch might do the trick and melt you?'

'Y-you have no right to talk to me like this—' She fought against his touch, knowing that she meant no more to him than a passing fancy. He missed Rachael, and to be alone with someone else acted as a spur, driving him to desires that bore no relation to love. 'You're behaving like a spoiled, arrogant boy!'

'Tell me,' his fingers pressed her little charms into her wristbone, almost deliberately, 'are you like Joyosa ... afraid of the desert in me?'

'No, it isn't that.'

'Then why don't you like me to touch you?'

'I—I don't belong to you because I wear your ring. I'm not your possession, here to amuse you when you feel the

128

need.'

'What if you were my ... possession?'

'I should still fight you.'

'You will tell me why.'

'Not if you were to beat me, *señor*.'

'You obstinate child! I suppose you are saving your kisses for a sedate young man who will never alarm you with too much passion, who will treat you as if you were any other piece of furniture in his neat and orderly home.'

'What nonsense, just because I won't be flirted with! It isn't fair of you——'

'To ruffle your chick-soft feathers, Miss Smith? Again I apologise. I shall remember in future that you find my proximity not much to your liking. My touch is far too primitive ... it might bruise that milky skin, and make untidy the fair hair and the prim white blouse. A word of advice, my pretence darling. Don't walk into my arms without looking; I might forget again that you are not my pretty possession.'

She was held by his dark eyes for a long tense moment. 'It's too easy to turn to someone when loneliness grips you, *señor*.'

'You think I am lonely?'

'It's a human enough feeling.'

'And you don't feel inclined to assuage the condition?'

'No.' She pulled away firmly this time, hurting her own wrist and glad of the pain. It excused the look she might have of wanting to break into tears. 'I'll get breakfast ... the sun is up and soon we should be on our way.'

'You sound quite anxious,' he drawled.

The sun above their heads was gilding the palm-tufts, and gone from the morning was that look of silent enchantment. Large birds winged across the blue sky, and the rolling dunes looked at a distance as if they had the feel of warm prickly velvet. A pagan, lonely land, which could bring out in two people travelling alone a primitive clash of emotions.

Don Raul strode to the car for his towel and shaving-kit. Janna went to the fire and stirred the warm embers that soon set burning some branches of dry tamarisk. Soon the coffee pot was bubbling, and she set out bread, butter, and apricot tarts for breakfast.

The *señor* joined her in about half an hour, clean-shaven, his hair wet and groomed, a sports shirt crisp against the brown skin of his throat and forearms. Janna poured him a cup of coffee, and kept her eyes pinned to his leather-strapped watch.

'The time is eight o'clock,' he said drily. 'We shall commence our journey as soon as we have eaten.'

'Have we much further to go?' She nibbled at the delicious crust on a slice of bread and butter.

'Quite a few miles, but we should arrive there about noon. Mmmm, you are beginning to make good coffee.'

'I watched to see how much you put into the pot last night. I'm glad you like it.'

'You are a funny girl.'

'I know I have a funny face.'

He smiled with his eyes. 'You know what I mean. You like to please people, but you retreat from them at the same time.' He bit into a tart with relish, a snap of strong white teeth that reminded her again of some superb feline, relaxed and yet dangerously alert, a purr and a snarl to his nature.

'It's a good thing we have almost reached El Amara. The food has almost run out, but for a little fruit.'

'So long as we have a supply of water, food is not the main problem in the desert. A travelling band of *bedouin* would always give us a meal, and I am also a fair shot and could wing us a couple of birds for dinner.'

'A couple of those?' She smiled and pointed upwards, to where big-winged birds were circling in a kind of sky ballet.

'Those are buzzards.' He grinned. 'A bit tough on the teeth. No, I refer to quail and pigeon.'

130

'How unkind to kill them for food.'

'Would you rather go hungry?' He quirked an eyebrow. 'I notice you are enjoying your breakfast, which means that our desert air agrees with you. Some European people feel a trifle under the weather when they first enter the garden of Allah.'

'I feel fine ... and I do like that description of the desert. One can almost imagine that biblical people still dwell among the sand dunes and the palm trees.'

'At El Amara you will find a garden of Eden.' He took from his belt a knife with a carved hilt and began to peel a large orange, cutting away the pith until the fruit gleamed enticingly. 'According to Spanish belief it was an orange which Eve gave to Adam. Will you accept half of this without letting your imagination run away with you?'

She held out her plate and held on to her smile. 'You don't look much like an Eve, *señor. Gracias.*'

'You don't believe that Adam was the innocent one! Your opinion of the male species seems to be that they are dangerous to know.'

'I imagine some are more dangerous than others,' she said demurely.

'And I wonder who heads the list?' he drawled.

She smiled and ate her segments of orange, finding them as sweet as honey. Were they this enjoyable because he had touched them? Not daring to meet his eyes, she let her gaze wander to the desert and saw that in daylight the sandstone rocks were a shade of red so that in contrast the sandhills looked like mounds of gold dust. Now the sun was really ablaze, spilling its warmth with such abundance that Janna could hardly believe the night had been so cold. She had snuggled down in the quilting of her sleeping-bag like a squirrel in its hideaway.

Now after her second cup of coffee she felt wide awake and ready for the trip ahead. Though apprehensive about meeting the Princess Yamila, she felt sure she would find El Amara a place after her heart. It was where Don Raul had grown up; where he had roamed the fruit groves, rode the Arab horses, and rebelled against the idea of having his wife chosen for him.

'If my kind of man is strange to you,' he said, quizzing her face as he lit a cigarette, 'think how much stranger your kind of woman is to me.'

She looked at him with eyes as wide and blue as the sky. 'I know I seem an oddity to you, *señor*. I wasn't trained from a child to please a man. I was taught to polish floors, to cook plain food, and eat humble pie.'

'Janna . . .' He spoke her name so deeply, made her desperately aware of the wonder of his eyes and their power to move her heart. She wanted to be taken into his arms, to be crushed and kissed, even if love was not his drive. She wanted to be shown affection, but even as she felt her need she was on her feet and bundling things into the hamper as if the *sirocco* had suddenly hit them.

He laughed, not heartlessly but with a kind of puzzlement. 'I am half inclined to keep you in the desert a few more days,' he said. 'I begin to glimpse what you are like beneath the icing.

'I don't think I'd fancy a diet of pigeon.' She marched to the car with the hamper and rug, calling over her shoulder: 'You might help a girl! I told you I'm no doe-eyed slave who lives only to please a lord and master.'

He came to her side with the rest of the camping gear, and she felt him smiling as he loaded the things into the car. 'You never know, *chica*. You might fall in love with a young man of El Amara and be only too eager to obey his every wish.'

'Life for such men must be quite a little heaven,' she said, infusing a tart note into her voice. 'They are made a fuss of by their women, but if anything displeases them they can say a few words of repudiation and the poor woman is divorced. I'll stay a spinster and open my tea-shop, if you don't mind?'

'I think I do mind.'

'Oh?'

'A girl without any relatives should have a desire for a family of her own.'

'I'll adopt a couple of cats,' she said lightly. And the next instant her attention was caught by a cloud of dust which seemed to be heading their way. 'What is it, señor? A sandstorm?'

He shielded his eyes with his hand and studied the approaching haze. Abruptly his face was stern and he spoke a word that sent a cold thrill down Janna's spine. 'Locusts! A horde of them, and heading for these palm trees, which they will strip bare!'

Even as he spoke he was thrusting Janna into the car and slamming the door. He had just reached the other side of the car when the locusts descended, a whirling cloud of winged monsters, making the strangest din as Don Raul threw himself in beside Janna. The creatures dived around the vehicle, covering the windows like a dust-sheet and making it impossible for the occupants to drive off.

'How awful!' Janna gasped. She covered her ears against the shrieking insects and watched as the windshield wiper began to hammer them back and forth without dislodging more than a few of the mass. Some had flown in through the windows before she had had time to close them, but Don Raul quickly disposed of the intruders.

'Fancy being out there in that seething whirlwind!' she whispered.

'Hide your eyes against me.' He pulled her head to his shoulder. 'They will be gone as soon as they have gorged on everything in the oasis.'

'I hope they aren't heading for El Amara.' She felt the warmth of his shoulder against her cheek, but it made her go cold to visualise that horde of greedy insects stripping bare the fruit trees of his home.

'One can't tell. They may be an isolated group flying through the desert on a foray, but if they are part of a larger more destructive force, then the groves could be in danger. Precautions are taken, the trees are sprayed with an insecticide which kills the creatures, but a dense mass of them can still cause a great deal of harm to the fruit harvest.'

'Oh, Raul!'

There was an acute silence within the car, a tenseness surrounded by the hungry clamour of hundreds of desert locusts. Janna's heart turned over ... she had only spoken his name and yet she had felt at once the stillness of him, a shock-wave almost, as if she had taken a liberty.

She drew away from him and stared from the window of the car ... the locusts were flying off, leaving the trees they had stripped of every leaf. Slowly the air cleared, their noise died away, and everything was still again. Like the calm following a whirlwind the silence was unbelievable, and then Janna gave a nervous start as the engine of the car sprang to life and they drove over the sand to the highway.

They were on their way; on the final lap of the journey to El Amara, and she was acutely aware of having touched a nerve when she had spoken his name without using the formal *señor*. She had made him aware of her as a person, perhaps, and not just as the girl hired to wear his ring, who amused him without touching his heart as he had touched hers.

He drove swiftly and silently, and Janna could not take her eyes from the grip of his hands on the wheel of the safari car. The knuckles showed taut and white under the sun-tanned skin.

She bit her lip. People weren't easy of understanding at the best of times, and Raul Cesar Bey was more complex than any of those she had met and known. She felt the pain of suppressed tears in her throat. Didn't he care for her sympathy? Didn't he want anything from her except the pleasure of teasing her.

CHAPTER TEN

THEY had been driving for several hours when the hot, tawny sands gave way abruptly to great *kasbahs* of rock. Feathery trees and flower-clumped vines hung in veils down the rocky walls of the canyon, and the shade and coolness was welcome after the miles of unrelieved heat.

Janna breathed excitedly, sensing that at last they drew near to El Amara. They drove out into the sun again and she blinked at the dazzle ... and then gave a murmur of delight as she caught sight of white-walled houses clinging like cubes of sugar to the lion-coloured hills. It came as a surprise to see civilised dwellings after so much space and emptiness, and only the occasional encampment of black *bedouin* tents.

'Soon you will see the groves of El Amara.' There was a note of expectation in the deep voice at her side. 'Because they repose in a valley, surrounded by all this rock which gives them shade and protects the moisture in the soil, they are unexpectedly lush and green.'

'I never dreamed of more than a large oasis, *señor.*'

'You are in for a surprise.' He laughed like a boy home-sick for what he loved. 'El Amara is the most unexpected place. Now we glimpse the first of the trees ... you see, the groves are like an immense fruit bowl.'

And there they were, massed abundantly around the steep, curving sides of the valley, filling it to the brim with the heady scents of citrus and tangerines, and the honey of a thousand ripening dates. A green wonder after the almost arid desert, and from the road above so immense. Janna pictured herself in that maze of fruit trees, wandering lost and never finding the way out.

'*Señor*, it's the most fantastic orchard I ever saw!'

'The rich green heart of El Amara. The source from which we draw our living and our sense of pride. From the harvest of fruit grows all the rest, the houses, the hospital,

135

the school, the chapel, and the mosque. We are a mixed community; the bells of the chapel mingle with the cry of the *muezzin*.'

'It's all so strange, so sudden,' she murmured, and now like a fly at the rim of a great fruit bowl the car was circling the groves in their natural valley. She had the sensation of holding on, and then realised with a catch of her breath that she was clinging to the edge of her seat. If their wheels should slip they would plunge over the rim of the road into that deep fragrant bowl.

Instead they turned suddenly and took a track that led into the sun again; the engine purred louder, they were going uphill and the houses were clustering in larger groups, curiously secretive, as if veiled against the eyes of a stranger. Janna felt bewildered. Where were the people? And then it came to her that most Eastern houses were enclosed by a wall, and that within the walls were tiled and flowery patios, women at their cooking and cleaning, children at their play, guarded from the world outside by the oriental love of mystery and intrigue. Only in their markets, in their public places, would these people meet to bargain and talk; to laugh and argue. In the evenings the women would lounge upon the flat roofs and eat honey cakes, while ibises flew gracefully against the pink sky and found nests on the rim of walls and in rock fissures.

'Thank heaven the locusts flew in another direction.' Janna felt dark eyes upon her profile, and tension crept back between her and the man who must soon present her to his family. She felt the falsity of her position more acutely than ever. It seemed that he wasn't yet ready to be called Raul by the girl he was supposed to desire.

'What is it, Janna? Are you nervous about meeting my grandmother?'

'Desperately. I—I don't want us to tell her an untruth. She doesn't deserve it.'

'You would rather I told her that her ward ran off with someone else, afraid of me because I am the grandson of a

Moorish princess?'

'In the end the Princess Yamila must be told.'

'The full story was never necessary and I won't tell her. She is a proud woman, with all her hopes centred in me. Better she believe an untruth than be hurt.'

'You need not tell her the whole truth.'

'She would find a way to learn it, perhaps from Rachael. I must protect them both.'

Because he loved them both, and Janna was only the girl he meant to use in his intrigue. He needed time in which to find the way to explain his true needs to his grandmother, and Janna would fill the gap and employ the mind of this proud old lady, who was looking forward to meeting a girl he might agree to marry. Even the Princess could not force his hand entirely, though Janna suspected that she tried. And loving his grandmother he strove to be as gentle and patient as his bold nature allowed.

Janna was tense with nerves, and at the same time beguiled by the magic of this place . . . her heart turned over when at last the car came in sight of the House of the Pomegranate.

It was more like a white-stoned palace set upon the ramparts of lion-coloured rock. Its walls gleamed among green palms and beaten-gold allamanda; it sprawled like a pasha among myrtles, plumbago and sheets of bougainvillea. And there along its high walls clustered the pomegranate trees, the red-gold fruits agleam among the leaves like hidden treasure.

A castle of dreams built on shifting sands for Janna, and she dared not voice her admiration. She must from this moment look unmoved by what her whole being longed to respond to.

'It's very nice,' she said politely.

Don Raul shot her a sharp look, and drove the car beneath a great stone archway into a courtyard fronting an immense door. A huge iron knocker hung in the centre of the door, and solid as a fortress were the walls in which it was set. There was no indication of the sumptuousness which Janna sensed behind that great arched entrance. The hanging gardens could not be seen from beneath the brow of the porch.

Dark as well were the brows of her pretence lover as he faced her, an arm resting on the wheel, the engine silent now but still giving off the warmth of their long drive. She looked at him from beneath her lashes and saw a rather sardonic twist to his lips.

'Welcome to El Amara,' he said. 'This house and its roof are at your feet, *señorita*.'

'How extravagant, *señor*!'

'We are extravagant people, so I hope when you see the interior of the house you will be a little warmer in your manner. The Princess will expect it. She lives in lovely surroundings, but that does not mean that she takes them for granted. She is Moorish. Her people like to give and receive compliments. It makes life more gracious.'

'I—I don't know when I am right and when I am wrong.' Janna gave voice to words that had simmered in her for the last miles of their journey. 'Am I to be cool or warm? Myself or someone else? Alice in the palace, or a chic young thing from the blue coast whom you pretend to fancy?'

He stared at her, his eyes narrowed to an unsmiling glitter. 'It isn't like you to be flippant, the usual sign that a woman is hurt and angry about something, but determined not to show it. What have I said or done to hurt your feelings?'

'I—I'm just a bit bewildered.' She tilted her chin and looked right at him, bracing herself against the usual shock to her feelings when his eyes looked into hers; so dark, holding tiny points of fire, and with a faint slant to the lids that made his glance so disturbing. It concealed more than it revealed, aided by the density of his lashes.

'And why are you bewildered, *niña*?'

'I don't know what you really want of me.'

'I want you to be yourself.'

'You mean it won't matter if I tell your grandmother I am a typist without any family?'

'She will be intrigued, and will want to make you welcome in our family circle.'

'Have you never brought home a girl like me before?'

'Never,' he drawled. 'It was not a practice of mine to bring home my girl-friends.'

'In case your grandmother saw one of them as your potential wife?'

'Do you imagine there were so many?' He leaned a little nearer to her, and she had that dizzying sensation of falling into his eyes. 'It would be enlightening to see inside your funny young head, where the cogs are busily spinning away, weaving sensational affairs for me out of a few casual remarks. Would you believe that Raul Cesar Bey has been more a lover of good horses than *houris*?'

'I'm not implying that you are a rake, but you are so——' There she broke off in confusion, while slowly his eyes filled with teasing laughter. Laugh creases formed attractively about his mouth, and the tip of her finger could have fitted into his chin cleft.

'Do go on, *chica*. I would give a diamond—a large one— to know what you really think of me.'

'Y—you know yourself that you aren't the most ugly man around.'

'There have been many men who were great lovers despite an odd sort of face. Some women, too, who were adored despite unattractive features. Good looks are not the sign of a Casanova nature. But I take it that because I happen to be the grandson of one of the most beautiful women in Morocco, I am therefore a bit of a libertine?'

'No.' The word broke from Janna. She wanted to touch his face—that dark, striking face that most women must look at with desirous eyes—and at the same instant she shrank from giving herself away to him. It would be embarrassing for both of them if he suspected that she had lost her heart to him. She would sooner pretend that he

139

meant no more to her than a sort of employer for whom she had agreed to work for a while.

'Don Raul, as if I'd have come this far if I thought you that sort of man. I just took it for granted that an attractive man of means had lots of girl-friends . . . I didn't mean to imply that you had lots of love affairs.'

'What would have been your reaction if I had turned out to be that sort of man? A cynical and sated satyr, and you alone with him in the desert?'

She broke into a laugh. 'I should have been terrified.'

'As it was, *chica*, you were nervous of my every glance. Do you imagine a man thinks of nothing but flirtation and lovemaking?'

'No, of course not!'

'You are blushing like mad.'

'Y-you are shameless, the way you tease a poor girl. You might remember, Don Raul, that I have never been so alone before with a man. I'm bound to find it a confusing experience—after Mildred.'

He laughed, and opened the car door beside him. 'Come, we will go indoors and present ourselves to the Princess. Someone will have seen the car approaching and she will be awaiting us with impatience.'

He held out a hand to Janna, who hesitated before allowing his lean fingers to clasp hers and draw her from the car into the hot sun falling on to the courtyard. She walked with him to the great front door of his home, and as if someone had been waiting on cue it swung open with a loud important clang and there in the aperture stood a porter in white. He bowed first to Don Raul, and then to his young companion, a flicker of quickly veiled interest in his eyes.

Don Raul spoke to him in Arabic, pointing to the car and indicating that their luggage be brought into the house. Then with a hand beneath Janna's elbow he led her across the interior patio of the house, around which in a crescent was built a cool, cloistered arcade with rooms beyond the fretted archways.

There were many flowers, twining around the tree-trunks and spilling from great stone jars. There was vivid tiling around the arcades and the picturesque fountain, with lotus buds afloat on the water of the basin. There was a sense of seclusion and beauty, ancient and Moorish, and yet appealing at once to Janna, the English girl who had known so much austerity and had never dreamed of seeing a place like this. A place out of an Arabian fable, unreal, and yet when she breathed, when she touched, when she looked, taking in everything with enchanted eyes, it was so alive, and the man beside her was plucking a mauve flower from a strange-looking tree.

In a casual way he tucked it into the neck of her blouse, where it nestled against her pale skin.

'What flower is it, *señor*?' She had gone weak a moment from the touch of his hand.

'A flower from the chaste-tree,' he drawled. 'My grandmother will take the hint, though your eyes give you away as a girl who has never had a lover.'

With a fast beating heart she let the flower remain where he had tucked it, and allowed herself to be led into the cloisters to a central archway. It framed a beautiful filigreed lamp, some lotus trees hung with small fruits, and floral tiling whose soft colours were repeated in the rugs that glowed against the floor of a cool and gracious room.

The carved furniture was of age-silkened wood, offset by brocaded divans, small tables with silver legs, and the delicate tracery of iron chandeliers hung from a ceiling of cedarwood. An oriental room with a Spanish flavour. A touch of the sensuous intermingled with the austere. An invitation to recline, and yet to wander among the various treasures displayed here and there on a table or a carved cabinet.

Janna took a vase into her hands and admired the smooth curves and lovely old patterns. She needed to feel calm and the feel of the vase helped a little. Don Raul was prowling the room like a supple tiger, almost purring his pleasure in everything, and Janna sensed that at any moment the

Princess Yamila would make her entrance through the archway at the other end of the *salon.*

'How good it feels to be home.' He reached up and set a jewelled lamp swinging on its chain. 'How unchanged everything is, not a cushion out of place, not a scent I haven't longed to breathe again. Breathe deep, Janna. That is the incense of a Moorish home.'

She glanced at him, as if casually, and all that he was struck through her like a thrill and a pain. So tall and strong and dark; a man who combined in his own nature the sensuous with a demanding selectivity. He wanted only the best of women . . . a Madonna, warm yet restrained; loving and brave, yet in need of his protection. Rachael was like that.

And Janna was suddenly afraid of what his grandmother might detect in her, the girl who was so unlike his ideal, but was young, innocent, fair, as his grandmother wished his wife to be. Suppose the Princess insisted that he marry her! How could he marry someone he didn't love . . . he had other plans, and they could go all wrong. Janna was again filled with the urge to run away before the Princess appeared. To put a stop to this game before it was too late.

She put down the vase, gave a hunted glance round the room, and suddenly fled towards the archway that gave on to the cloisters. She reached them and was a white figure running among their shadows when she heard the swift padding of feet behind her. She was near a column when he overtook her, when his hands reached for her and swung her around roughly to face him. His eyes were angry as she struggled to get away from him, there beside a column smothered in the leaves and flowers that twined down over the roof of the cloisters. She felt herself thrust among them; she looked up desperately into Raul's dark eyes, she felt his touch to her bones.

'What are you doing?' he asked. 'Where do you think you are going?'

'I can't pretend—not to your grandmother.'

'Did I ask you to pretend to be headlong in love with me?' He shook her, there against the mass of flowers and leaves.

'Y-you don't understand——'

'Of course I do.' He snapped the words. 'You are scared our deception will lead to marriage, but I assure you it won't. I would allow neither of us to become that involved.'

'How can you be so sure——?' She gazed up at him, her hair flopping softly in her eyes, a top button of her blouse pulled open when he had grasped her so roughly, the chaste flower still caught and held there against the pale warmth of her skin. She felt the rake of his eyes over her exposed neck, taking in the disorder he had brought about. She saw his mouth form into a sort of smile . . . tigerish, showing the white line of his teeth.

'You shrink like that violet flower from the very thought of having me for a husband, eh? My touch is hardly bearable to you . . . I can feel you trembling, shaking the leaves. Poor child,' he taunted, 'no wonder you want to run away. But where will you go? Out there is a desert city you hardly know, and beyond it the many miles of desert and ocean that separate you from England. You have to stay, *chica*. You have to go through with what we have started. The Princess knows you are here and you have to meet her.'

'Please——' Janna felt crushed by what he believed, that she disliked his touch and couldn't bear the thought of actually marrying him. What she couldn't bear was the possibility of being forced upon him . . . he would hate her for that.

'Please?' he softly mocked. 'You want me to let you go?'

'Yes.' She had to say the word, when with all her being she longed to be held by him, roughly or tenderly. If there had been no Rachael, she would have let happen whatever had to happen to a girl who loved a man as much as she did.

'I will let you go when I have your promise that you won't do anything foolish.'

'Foolish?' she echoed.

'Such as finding someone whom you think will convey

you safely across the desert, out of my reach.'

'How can I promise not to do that? You know I might feel forced into it——'

'You will be forced into no marriage with me,' he said explosively. 'I would no more marry you than I would a—a doll. I want no loveless thing in my life. Do you understand?' He shook her again, and then as if his anger could be expressed only in punishment he bent his head and she gave a little pained cry as he crushed her close to him and buried his lips in the warm disclosed hollow of her shoulder. She was lost in the leaves and flowers, in his hard arms, and the warm power of his body. She felt he might break her as he bent her over his arm and forced her lips to meet his. Deep, then deeper, until she clung reeling to the strong shoulders and let him expend his anger in the age-old way.

Abruptly he pushed her away from him, and she saw his eyes close heavy-lidded, while a pulse beat like mad beside his mouth. A strand of black hair lay snared in the warm heat of his forehead. He looked to her like a tiger disturbed.

'You asked for that.' He spoke as if he hated her. 'If I can't have your promise to stay until *I* can take you away again, there may be more of the same. I can't spank you . . . or perhaps I can.'

His eyes dwelt consideringly upon her tense young face, then before she could retreat he reached out and pulled her towards him. With easy strength he swung her over his shoulder, and her teeth bit down on her lip as he gave her a stinging little slap on her backside. He strolled with her towards the *salon*, and aroused to fury by his treatment of her, she caught at his hair and gave it a fierce tug.

'You brute!'

He laughed, as if enjoying himself. 'You will give me that promise, little tigress, or else.'

'I'm not intimidated by you!'

'Brave words,' he scoffed. 'You know that next time in my arms you might learn a more profound lesson . . . and it might be quite a pleasure to teach you.'

'You wouldn't dare!'

'I would, *berida*, and you know it.'

She fell silent as she contemplated his threat, and when they reached the *salon* she felt the indignity of being kissed without mercy, slapped on her rear end, and carried into the house like a sack of goods.

'I hate you!' she stormed, knowing herself a liar.

He was laughing when a woman spoke in a deep, smiling, indulgent voice. 'How appropriate, my grandson, that you return home with the girl slung across your shoulder. I am most entertained. It has been a long time since those old cloisters were so enlivened by the chase and the capture of a young woman by a determined man. My dearest Raul, I would not have missed such a scene for anything.'

Janna found herself lowered to her feet, and never had she felt so ruffled, or so embarrassed. She raised a hand to smooth her hair, feeling the wild pink in her cheeks as she met the amused eyes of the Princess Yamila; the woman who held sway over the people of El Amara, who was renowned for her beauty, and who lived to see her greatest wish fulfilled . . . her grandson's marriage.

She was clad in a swathed dress of silver-purple brocade, and an ornament of beaten silver adorned her gown and held in place her head veil. Her face was a gracious oval set with dark radiant eyes, her skin was softly amber, and set in her right nostril was a glittering jewel. She must as a young woman have been ravishingly lovely; even yet she retained much of her beauty and a queenly grace.

She held out her hands to her grandson, and Janna noticed the lacework of henna on them . . . she knew that henna was for joy, the joy of the Princess in having Raul Cesar Bey with her again.

He went to her and kissed each hand in turn, then he embraced her, drawing the slight, silken figure against his broad chest. He spoke to her in Arabic, his voice pitched low and loving. Janna watched their meeting with a certain wistfulness. How wonderful to be as sure of his love as the Princess Yamila, who might try to boss him, but who had a firm and everlasting hold on his heart. She had taken the place of his parents, and for her sake he brought Janna to El Amara.

The novelty of the English girl would engage her interest, and the anger she might feel towards Joyosa would be lessened by having in Janna a possible bride for her grandson. Janna was worried about the role imposed on her, but she could not retreat from it. Don Raul was looking at her, a warning glitter in his eyes. He was about to present her to his grandmother, and his look demanded that she fall in with his wishes. There was nothing else to do, and she felt a tremor in her knees as she approached the Princess Yamila.

Don Raul spoke in English as he presented Janna. 'We met in a garden, Princess. I thought you might like her, so I persuaded her to come to El Amara for a holiday. Her name is Janna. She is English and rather shy of me, but also rather beguiling, eh?'

His grandmother gazed frankly at Janna, taking in the elfin slant of her cheekbones, the youth and uncertainty still apparent in her features. 'You could almost, Raul, have passed this girl off as my ward.' The Princess held out her hands in welcome to Janna, who took them hesitantly, feeling the rings, the delicate veins, and the surprising strength. 'You are unusual to us, my dear. So very fair, and so blue-eyed. I can understand why Raul brought you to see me—but did he bring you a little against your will?'

Janna blushed at this amused reference to being flung slim and helpless over Raul's broad shoulder. 'When Don Raul told me of you, Princess, I wanted very much to meet you.'

'Did you not fall in love, first, with this handsome devil?'

'No—that is——' Janna was confused by the frankness of his grandmother. 'We are just friends——'

'Are you, child? I thought he brought you here in place of the girl I hoped he might marry. Raul knows he must marry someone, and he is being obstinate.'

'Men don't like to give up their freedom, Princess.'

'We women have to surrender ours, and we are not allowed the indulgence of a lover if the marriage is loveless.' The Princess cast a keen glance at her grandson. 'The girl is pleasing, but she is also a vulnerable one. Are you aware of this, *my queridisimo*? Do you see beyond the soft white skin and the deep blue eyes?'

He flicked a look over Janna, and she felt almost shocked, as if on a slave block being considered by a potential master. He didn't love her, but how far was he prepared to go in order to please the Princess? He had said to marry her would be like marrying a doll, but supposing the Princess persuaded him . . . because she, Janna, had soft skin, blue eyes, and an all too apparent innocence? Janna wasn't so entirely innocent that she didn't know that a man could feel desire without being in love with the woman he desired. Only a while ago in the shadow of the cloisters he had kissed her, and the ground rocked again beneath her feet as she recalled those long, lost moments in his arms.

'I see only that my young friend is wearied by our long trip across the desert, Princess.' He smiled into Janna's eyes, confusing her anew. 'We met with a horde of locusts and we both feared they might descend on the groves. Has Ahmed been keeping the men alert? This is the time of the year when we could lose much of our harvest if the locusts came in force.'

'It would be a disaster!' At once the attention of the Princess was diverted from Janna, and she was grateful. Did Raul realise how she felt, and was he truly sympathetic? She had been a lonely little fool, to have allowed his fascination to bring her this far from home. She could have left Mildred of her own accord and returned to the security of England; to a job in a typing pool where one was safely anonymous.

'I think,' he said, 'that Janna would like to rest in her room while we discuss business.'

The Princess smiled her agreement, and a manservant in

white appeared to conduct her to another section of the house; an apartment opening on to a small patio, and so lovely that Janna sensed at once that she had been placed in the rooms set aside for Joyosa. Her suitcases were open on a table at the foot of the low, wide ottoman bed, silk-covered and with a netting canopy let down from an ivory ring affixed to a ceiling painted with tiny golden stars.

Her hand sank into the bed, and her feet were deep in the pile of a topaz yellow carpet. There was a pearl-inlaid dressing table with a matching wardrobe. A divan heaped with cushions, exquisite screens and doorways, filigreed lamps, a tall water-jar filled with white flowers, and the sound of birds in her own private patio.

Janna would have been an ungrateful girl if she had not responded to the seclusion and beauty of her surroundings ... she suppressed the shy thought that the place was not unlike a *seraglio* where she awaited her master.

She stepped through a fretted archway and there at her feet almost lay a sunken bath lined with Arabian tiles. Little wisps of warm steam curled up from the water, which some-one had run in expectation of the *lella* wishing to bathe. Huge Turkish towels were laid out on a low table beside the bath, and there was a painted looking-glass on a stand, a box of cosmetics, and an arabesqued chest full of silk things.

'My *seraglio*,' Janna murmured, and one by one her fingers were unbuttoning her blouse and the blue-dotted tie. A mauve flower fell to the blue and gold tiles and lay near the foot she had slipped out of her sandal. She prodded the flower with her toes and it fell into the shimmering water. A moment later Janna slipped into the pool, a slim white figure reflected in the painted mirror ... soft-skinned, inviting the touch of a lean, sun-bitten hand. Soft hair clinging to a slender nape. The slight tilt of breasts guarding a quickening heart as someone came through the archway into the bath room.

It was a girl carrying a tray, which she set down on one

148

of the inlaid tables. She cast a lash-veiled glance at Janna, who was soaping herself madly in an effort to hide her nudity. A smile came and went on the girl's lips, and she pointed to the tray, on which stood a pot giving off a delicious aroma of hot chocolate, a silver jug of cream, a dish of cakes, and several large and luscious-looking peaches.

'Thank you.' Janna had forgotten the Arabic words for thanks. *'Gracias.'*

The girl giggled, then evidently aware that the English *lella* would prefer to be alone while she bathed, she went away, and Janna sighed her relief. Arabian front doors might have huge keys to keep them locked, but all the other doors seemed designed to let anyone in. Raul himself might take it into his head to stroll in upon her while she bathed!

Janna splashed about in the water as if to drown her thoughts, but a sly one kept taunting her. Suppose this was her *seraglio*? Anything might be laid on for the adored grandson of the Princess!

Half frightened, she stepped out of the bath and wrapped herself in a great towel. Her cheeks were a wild pink, and her hair clung in drifts of gold about her neck. Her shoulders were pale and dewed with droplets of water. She didn't dare to think of what Raul would do if he saw her like this, and she glanced around timidly, as if she heard him approaching and sought some means of hiding from him. Her hands clutched the towel closer; she was sure she heard footsteps on the tiles of the patio, and a moment later the drifting smoke of a cigarette was no illusion. Raul was out there . . . and she was in here, clad in very little!

She glanced about for her clothes, but they were gone! The girl must have taken them, and Janna almost tripped over the towel in her haste to examine the chest of silk things. She found a full-length robe of silk brocade and put it on, her fingers full of nerves as she buttoned it from her throat to the hem. She turned to the mirror. The brocade was a soft turquoise, with something of gold in the material when she moved. She noticed how the colour became her, and her feeling of shyness was intensified. She gave a start when a deep voice called her name from the patio.

'Won't you come and join me?'

She had never felt more shy of him than right now. They had travelled together in the desert, and spent a night there beneath the stars, but now she was in his home, and clad in something of Arabian silk that made her look and feel a stranger to herself.

'Janna?'

She hesitated, then picked up the tray of refreshments and carried them out to the patio, where he lounged in a long wicker chair, his legs stretched out, smoke drifting about his dark head, looking utterly at home.

He smiled lazily when he saw her, letting his gaze wander all the way down the long line of tiny pearl buttons to her bare feet.

'You have forgotten your slippers,' he drawled.

'The tiles are warm.' She crossed over to him, carrying the tray and feeling like a barefoot slave about to wait on him.

'The Arabian clothes become you, *berida*.'

'Don't—please!'

'My dear girl, what am I doing now?'

'Looking at me as if I'm a sort of slave girl.'

'Perhaps it is the atmosphere.' He smiled wickedly. 'This apartment and adjoining court were used long ago by the favourite of an ancestor of mine—a practice not entirely out of fashion.'

'Is that why I have been put here?'

'Don't you find it attractive—and secluded?'

'It's very nice.' Her heart missed a beat at his use of the word secluded. 'I imagine it was prepared for Joyosa . . . what did you tell your grandmother with regard to her truant ward?'

'I told her Joyosa preferred another man . . . and that I preferred another woman.'

Janna stared at him, and she just had to sit down on the

150

tiled rim of the fountain before her knees gave way. 'Did she think you meant me?'

'I imagine so.' He took a honey cake and bit it neatly in half. 'Now don't look at me in such an alarmed way—I have never known a girl so unflattering as you—I have promised that you will not have forced upon you a fate you shrink from.'

She gave him a quick look, and then poured a cup of chocolate.

'You know what I mean,' he drawled. 'Bending your head so I can't read your eyes.'

'This is delicious chocolate,' she said irrelevantly.

'Rather sweeter than the thought of having Raul Cesar Bey as a husband, eh?'

There was no answer to that one, and the birds twittered in the pepper trees as Janna drank her chocolate, and let this man believe the only thing possible. Colourful bee-eaters roved among the flowers; the flame hibiscus, the white geraniums, and scented shrubberies of jasmine.

The courtyard of the favourite!

What was Raul thinking as his eyes brooded upon the scene? That if Rachael were here with him the patio would be perfect in its seclusion?

CHAPTER ELEVEN

JANNA had been at El Amara a week, and this particular morning she felt like exploring the village that lay on a slope of the lion-coloured rock, small houses amid groves, and tiled minarets.

The air was heavy with sunshine and the scents of ripening fruit. There was a sound of trickling streams watering the many trees, and here and there in the groves a song was heard, old and sweetly melancholy. The secretive little houses clung to the rock, and occasionally a door was ajar and Janna caught glimpses of stone courts, and women at work in them, the glint of silver below the hem of long dresses and the tinkle of a bell or a charm on the anklets they loved to wear. They were amber-skinned, and their dusky eyes dwelt curiously upon Janna when she gave way to impulse and glanced into the courtyards.

She smiled beneath the brim of the floppy straw hat, and very often a pair of dark eyes smiled back at her.

El Amara . . . a place to love, and she had to guard each day against falling too deeply beneath its spell. Its sunsets were glowing wonders, and the fretted minarets stood against the blue and bronze sky like carvings in lace. Ardent, dreamy, alluring desert city. Janna wandered in it, breathing its aromas as if to store them up for the future; filling her eyes with all its strangeness, knowing that her few weeks here must suffice for a lifetime.

She came at last to the village market, where the hillside peace gave way to noise and bustle, and aromas more tangy. The people knew who she was and she received polite bows from the robed men, and was not pestered at every step to purchase a bowl or a pumpkin or a leather bag. She was the young lady from the house of the Princess; the young master's *lella*, and if she chose to wear a straw hat and a pink trouser-suit then that was all right with them, if a little amazing. The young Bey could have insisted on the *baracan* and veil.

Janna knew what thought lay behind the glances that followed her into the alley of spices, where the fragrant mint was mixed with bunches of herbs and where she could have lingered an hour, just breathing the air. She wandered on, slim and nonchalant in her pink apparel, the *lella* of Raul Cesar Bey . . . and where was he this fine morning?

She had left him going over the accounts for his grandmother, a white shirt open at his throat, and clad still in the breeches and boots of his early morning ride on Sultan, the Arab horse of glistening red-brown, with a wicked gleam in its eye.

Someone wandered by carrying the odd-looking vegetables of an Arabian market in the hood of his *jellabah*. A merchant cleaned his copper goods with lemon and sawdust, and stabs of sunlight came through the osier awning overhead and caught the sheen on the bowls and vases. Janna paused to admire a graceful tea-pot with a round body, a long elegant spout and a slender handle affixed to a lid shaped like a pagoda.

It looked magical, as if a delicious brew would pour from it. She smiled and pointed it out to the merchant. 'How much?' she asked, for these wily men knew that question in any language, and this was not the *souk* of Benikesh, where she had been a young tourist to be robbed.

A price was named and after a little friendly bargaining she walked off with the tea-pot . . . the first item with which to start her teashop in that quiet seaside resort. How different was all this! Two distinct worlds, and in her heart she wanted this one far more than any other. Everything was so alive, so spicy, and unusual. She watched silver boxes being hammered in the street of silversmiths, and saw lanterns wrought from copper and fitted with panels of jewel-coloured glass. She was tempted to buy some little spiced sausages, smoking hot on a skewer, but caution prevailed and she bought instead a bag of almonds in the shell.

She strolled away from the market place and found herself beneath the swooping boughs of palm trees at the edge of the village. The desert lay beyond the rocky ramparts of El Amara, and she perched on a tawny rock and ate her almonds, crunching them in small teeth as milky as the nuts themselves. She was unaware of her own casual charm, her straw hat tilted back from her eyes, the palm trees shading her pink-clad figure.

She was aware only of this strangely beautiful place in the desert, the tangy stillness, the caress of coolness beneath the crescent branches of the trees. Some wild oleanders splashed the tawny cliffs with crimson petals, and the desert beyond was an inscrutable golden mask. The people of El Amara were like their desert, fascinating but not easily conquered. They were fierce, and also tranquil, with a Kismet attitude to life. What was written would inevitably cast its spell.

Absorbed in her thoughts she was startled when a hand touched her shoulder. She turned quickly and found herself gazing upwards into the velvety black eyes of Don Raul's cousin, Ahmed. He was clad in a light, well-tailored suit, but he wore the traditional head-covering bound by ropes of silk. He smiled, a flash of fine teeth against the smooth olive skin and the slender black moustache across his upper lip.

'This is a pleasure, Janna, to find you alone for once. I said to myself, no one else could look so pretty and pensive at one and the same time.'

'Hullo, Ahmed.' She smiled and held out the bag of nuts. 'Will you have one?'

'If you don't mind I will sit beside you and smoke a cheroot.' He suited action to his words, and she felt the lean agility of his body as he shared the rock ledge with her and took from his breast pocket an onyx case that gleamed in his long fingers. He had hands more delicate than Raul's; features more Arabian. His mother came from the city of Fez, a charming woman who loved to gossip about all things feminine. Ahmed's sister, Leila, was married with a baby, and all of them lived at the House of the Pomegranate and had their own apartments. It seemed a Moroccan-Spanish tradition to share a spacious roof with congenial relatives.

Janna, who had never known a family, found the arrangement a lively one. It was fun to live among people who laughed, and argued, and made the evenings so rich in new experiences for her. Having overcome their surprise at her arrival in place of Joyosa, they now accepted her, and Ahmed seemed especially intrigued by her English looks, and the novelty of her shyness in contrast to the boldness of Raul.

'And what have you been doing all the morning?' he

asked. 'Some sightseeing and a little shopping?'

'Yes. I was intrigued by the market place, and I bought this tea-pot to start off my tea-shop when I——' There in some confusion she broke off, for Ahmed was looking at her with narrowed eyes through his cheroot smoke.

'You intend to start a tea-shop, Janna?'

'Well, it's a sort of joke between Don Raul and myself.'

'Is it possible that you don't really wish to marry him?' Ahmed leaned forward and looked into her eyes. 'You always refer to him as Don Raul, as if you are half afraid to use his name alone. Are you afraid of my cousin?'

'No, of course not. Why should you think such a thing?'

'You seem to me to be always a little nervous of being alone with him. You are alone this morning, and I should have been delighted to show you around El Amara.'

'You don't consider me afraid of you, Sheik Ahmed?'

He smiled warmly, and looked most attractive. 'I should not want to frighten you away from me. It came as a most pleasing surprise when Raul brought you to us instead of that other girl. She was a little show-off, and I remember well the occasion when she made her pony bolt so Raul would ride after her in front of a crowd of our people. She set her cap for him from the very start.'

'But I thought . . . he told me she didn't want him and that was why she ran away with someone else.'

'Raul was just being gallant in saying she ran away from him. The truth is the reverse . . . in an attempt to make him look the unwanted one she found some young man to elope with. I know Raul too well. He is my cousin, and we have shared hunting trips as well as work. He never intended to be the bridegroom of any woman whom he did not choose for himself, but being deeply fond of our grandmother he made it seem as if he were willing to fall in with her wishes. She is usually shrewd about people, but in the case of Joyosa she seemed a little dazzled by the girl's fair beauty.'

Ahmed's velvety gaze stroked Janna. 'Now I have met you, I understand how it is possible to fall under the spell of

155

blue eyes. In this part of the world a man sees only brown eyes.'

'Do you think you ought to be talking like this to Don Raul's girl?' she asked lightly. 'He is very possessive, and very strong.'

Ahmed gave a soft laugh. 'You are not a girl to go running to my cousin with tales. You care too much about people to wish them harm.'

'And you think that gives you the freedom to . . . flirt with me?'

'I am only being friendly, Janna. I have seen for myself that Raul has an unnerving effect on you. I have watched you when we are all together, and you avoid being close to him, you shrink from his touch, you are a girl faced by a dilemma.'

'I—I merely feel a stranger in new surroundings,' she said defensively. 'You have no right to assume from my manner that I am scared of Don Raul. Would I have crossed the desert with a man I felt unsafe with? Hardly!'

'Are English girls shy of revealing their feelings in public?'

'Aren't the girls of your country equally shy? I have heard that many of them don't meet their fiancé until the day of the marriage.'

'That custom is dying out. Now we meet more and more, and decide our own destinies.'

'You are very modern in your outlook, Sheik Ahmed.'

'Yes, more so in a way than Raul. He has a Spanish backbone.'

'You mean he has a rigid code of honour and that having set his mind and his heart on someone, he will settle for nothing less?'

'Yes, he is a believer in a lifelong love, a Latin in far more ways than Leila or myself.'

'You are a romantic, Sheik Ahmed, but he believes in one love, one union, one close tie for always with the woman he marries?'

'A little frightening, is it not, to be so intense about it? That is why I can sympathise with the doubts you may now be feeling, Janna. So demanding a man must make you quail.'

Her gaze dwelt upon the surrounding desert. She only quailed because she was not the one on whom Don Raul had set his heart, to take, to love, to hold for always in his arms. She had felt in him this intensity of purpose, this desire for a complete giving and receiving, and she thought Doña Rachael the luckiest of women. She could visualise nothing more wonderful than to be the centre and soul of Raul's life.

'Perhaps,' she said quietly, 'I feel not quite able to live up to his ideal. But you mustn't say anything to the Princess. She mustn't be told just yet that nothing is settled between Don Raul and myself.'

'I can be the soul of discretion.' Ahmed took her hand and studied the flawless Romanos emerald. 'You should wear a sapphire, not a great green stone that weighs upon your small hand. A blue stone set in pearls, to match your eyes and your skin.'

'Please——' She pulled her hand free of his. 'What I should really like is to go and have something to eat. Your desert air makes me feel ravenous.'

'Would you enjoy a real Arabian meal?' He stood up and drew her to her feet; she reached just to his shoulder and was aware of his attractive personality, his romantic good looks, his relaxed air of being a young man who enjoyed life as it came.

'Where do you intend to take me for this Arabian meal?' she asked with a smile.

'To the Café Moresque, where the kebabs are as tender as your heart, and the quail as delectable as your smile.'

'Poor quail, netted to please us greedy humans!'

'You do amuse me, Janna.' Laughing, he led the way down the rocky incline towards the centre of El Amara. 'No one but you would feel so sorry for birds that fall prey to the falcons anyway.'

'It is more natural,' she argued. 'They are on the wing and might get away.'

'You would sooner be caught on the wing than captured in a net?' He gave her a keen look. 'Are you planning to run away from Raul?'

'As if I'd dare do that!'

'If you are thinking of flight, then I might agree to help you. I don't like to see you so on edge, so obviously nervous of him. You are afraid, Janna, of marriage with a man who would make you his netted quail.'

'We both agreed that he believes in a marriage of love.'

'You are saying that he does not love you?'

'You have keen eyesight, Ahmed. You must have seen for yourself that he doesn't.'

'Perhaps I have been looking more at you, a girl so nice that I took it for granted he wanted you. Why else, Janna, did he bring you to El Amara?'

'To make up to the Princess for not bringing Joyosa. He was afraid she would be disappointed, perhaps angry with Joyosa's family. I—I understand that she can be very angry when her will is crossed.'

'Too true. The Princess is in a position of authority, and we have always spoiled her and bowed to her whims. Yes, she might well have given way to temper, and to do so is not good for her heart. She had a slight failure of the heart a few months ago and was ill for some time. When she recovered she began to worry Raul to take a wife. And he, worried in case she made herself ill again, departed for France with the promise that he would bring Joyosa home with him—if she would come. I knew already that on a previous visit to the Côte d'Azur, when he went to arrange a financial matter for Doña Rachael Corleza, whom he may have mentioned to you, he saw Joyosa and made it plain that he had no feeling of any sort for her. Raul can be frank to the point of pain, and he can also be secretive. Joyosa could take the truth, but he loves the Princess. A jolt to her delicate heart and he might lose her. He loves her as only a Latin can—intensely. There is much he would do to make her content, but I doubt if he could have brought himself to marry her flighty young ward. A pretty creature but empty-headed. You are the opposite to her in many ways.'

He seemed to say this significantly, and it was a relief when they reached the palmy centre of El Amara. A few minutes later they paused outside the Café Moresque, a large attractive café with tables set beneath a shady awning, where several European visitors were enjoying the Eastern cuisine and taking an interest in the passers by. Janna felt their gaze as she and Ahmed sat down at one of the tables, which was the immediate centre of bowing waiters.

'Shall I order for you?' asked Ahmed, looking very much a personage with his fine face, his impeccable clothes, and the attention of the staff without the raising of his smallest finger. Janna wondered what the tourists were thinking as they glanced from her fairness, as she removed her hat, to the Arabian headwear of her companion.

She smiled at him. 'Order me something I shall remember.'

He met her eyes for an intent moment, then he consulted with the waiters and she was free to let her thoughts roam over the things he had said about Raul.

He had confirmed her own anxiety . . . that in order not to cause further distress to the Princess he might fulfil her wish to see him married as soon as possible . . . and Janna was actually here in El Amara, while Doña Rachael was miles away.

Marriage with herself would not give Raul what he truly wanted, but it would please his grandmother. And despite Janna's love for him, she had no desire for a marriage of pure convenience. Raul was a Latin, for whom marriage was for always, and she would be his regret rather than his reward.

Something had to be done, and Ahmed had reawakened

her desire to flee from El Amara before Raul persuaded her to stay and marry him . . . she knew he could, because she knew her own heart and how much she longed to be with him. But without the woman of his heart he would never be happy, and above all things Janna wanted him to find joy and contentment. She would sooner slip out of his life than stay to be the bride he chose for his grandmother's sake rather than his own.

If she ran away it would simplify the situation. The Princess would not wish another flighty girl upon him . . . she would accept Rachael and realise when she saw them together that he had made the only right and happy choice.

In a quiet mood she ate saffron-tinted *cous-cous*, then lamb kebabs with tiny marrows and green beans, and finally fruit with date cream.

'That was delicious, Ahmed.' She conjured a smile, but her heart felt heavy at the thought of leaving a place such as El Amara. She felt at home here. She liked the people, the hot sun gilding the dome of the mosque, the tiled doorways, and the shadows of the palms. She felt alive here, and of some account, but in order to ensure Raul's future happiness she had to leave it all behind and return to the loneliness of a bedsitter and a typewriter. There would be no tea-shop after all; she couldn't bear the thought of accepting money for having come here. She would leave secretly, with no goodbyes, and Raul would guess that she left him free to marry Rachael.

'Your eyes are sad.' Ahmed sat looking at her with a kind and questioning smile. 'A woman is supposed to be content after being fed upon the fruits of El Amara.'

'I am considering your offer, Ahmed. I think I should like to go away quickly and quietly—if you will help me?'

'Ah, then my guess was a correct one—you are afraid of a forced marriage with Raul. You wish to leave El Amara without him knowing?'

'Yes—it would be for the best,' she said quietly, her gaze bent to her coffee cup. 'Could you arrange it for me?'

'I could do better than that, Janna. I could take you.'

'Really?' Her eyes met his. 'If Raul found out, he would be very angry.'

'I expect he will guess that I am the culprit, but in both of us there is a dash of the devil and we have had fights before.'

'Over a girl?' She half smiled.

He laughed. 'More often over a horse we both favoured, and once when I shot a gazelle by mistake. Upon that occasion he almost broke my jaw.'

'He may be equally angry if you conduct me across the desert to Benikesh, where I can take the train. Are you prepared for that?'

'I admire you, Janna.'

'It seems hardly worth the risk, for a girl you have known only a week.'

'Some people we know better in a week than in a year. I know what sort of a girl you are—you want those you are fond of to be happy, and you can see no happiness in a marriage of reluctance. Tell me frankly, are you running away from a man you fear, or a man you love?'

'I would hardly run away if I—loved Raul.'

'I think you are the sort of girl who would run away for exactly that reason. You would not marry just to have security and a good home. There is a saying that the cool night harbours a warm day, here in the desert. The white flower often has a golden heart.'

'Meaning?' Her lips trembled against the rim of her coffee cup.

'You would no more be content with a cool and polite marriage than Raul himself. Won't you tell him to his face that you wish to go away?'

'I could—but he can be persuasive.'

'You are afraid you might give in to him, as you gave in when he met you in France and talked you into coming here —in place of Joyosa?'

'Yes.'

'Then you must be very fond of him, if you are afraid of yourself rather than of him.'

'I—I don't want to discuss my feelings, Ahmed. I just want to have arranged as soon as possible a way of—escape. It sounds melodramatic, I know, but if you are willing to take me, then I should be deeply grateful. There is no one else I can ask. No one else I dare to ask. I don't want him to find out that I plan to leave. I just want to make the break as swiftly and finally as possible.'

'Then I suggest the evening of our grandmother's birthday party, when most of his attention will be upon her. We could drive away in my car to Dafni, a town about forty miles from here where I can arrange for a private plane to take you all the way to Casablanca.'

'I—I haven't a great deal of money, Ahmed.'

'It would be my pleasure to pay your passage.'

'Why do you wish to help me? What is your real reason?'

'I don't like to see you unhappy.'

'No, there is more to it than that. I wonder if you don't like Raul and would like to pay him out for something.'

Ahmed slowly shook his head as he lit a cheroot and puffed smoke at a hovering wasp. 'The truth is that I admire Raul very much. He is the man destined to take charge of things here—already he is the nominal head of El Amara—and I feel that he must have a contented home life if he is to be the governor of vision and enterprise which we need in order to expand and develop into a really progressive province. I know that Raul has many new schemes up his sleeve, but there is a side to him which needs the close companionship, the love and devotion of a wife of his heart. If Raul has this, then there is nothing he will not accomplish for El Amara. We live, Janna, in an age of political upheaval and rebellion, and Raul will hold the loyalty and love of our people if his own personal happiness is centred here, for him to return to at the end of each day.'

'To the woman he loves,' Janna said quietly. 'To the one on whom he has set his heart.'

162

'Exactly. Raul is unlike me. I am a romantic man of the East and I find my happiness more easily. He has a strong sense of responsibility, and with the right woman by his side he will be perfect for El Amara.'

'You love El Amara more than any woman, Ahmed?'

'It is in my blood, Janna, the love of the land, but I lack Raul's power of administration. He is born to be our governor.'

She smiled wistfully at Ahmed. 'So your motive in helping me to run away from him is that you don't think I am right for him?'

'You could be right for me, Janna.'

'No——' The word broke from her. 'No, just help me to leave him—as soon as the time is right.'

'The night of the party, I promise you.' He reached across the table and patted her hand. 'In the meantime I will contact my friend at Dafni and arrange to have a private plane standing by. It should not take more than an hour for us to reach the airfield in my car, and you should be on your way before Raul notices you are gone.'

She went cold in the sunshine at the prospect of never seeing Raul again . . . Raul who would hardly notice when she slipped away from the party. It was to be more than a family occasion. Everyone else in El Amara would celebrate the birthday of the Princess. There was to be a riding fantasia, gifts for the children, a feast, and a firework display. It wasn't every day that the 'mother' of El Amara became seventy years young, and Janna could imagine how easy it would be that night for her to slip away with Ahmed.

'You are right,' she said to him. 'A man in authority can be lonely, unless he has at the centre of his life the woman born to be his companion and his contentment. I am not the one for Raul. I have known it since the first day I saw him.'

'And where was that?' Ahmed's velvety dark eyes could look very sympathetic, and Janna was sure it was no idle rumour that he had a couple of pretty sweethearts. His sister

163

Leila was always teasing him about being fond of the girls and much more of a flirt than Raul. If Janna had ever thought Raul a raffish man-about-the-world, she was learning that at El Amara he was very much a man of purpose.

Ahmed could find happiness more easily than Raul, but he was ambitious for El Amara and he knew that his cousin must find his deeper, more profound contentment if this lovely desert province was to continue in peace, and to flourish in the future. Don Raul was the man for the job, but he would strive all the harder if he married the right woman.

'We met in a hotel garden.' Janna smiled with nostalgia. 'He was with Doña Rachael Corleza at the time.'

'Ah yes, Rachael. She is a charming person. Raul has always been very fond of her and her children.'

Janna played with a pellet of bread and kept her eyes lowered. Ahmed understated it. Raul was more than fond of his Latin Madonna, with huge eyes filled with tears. Tears because he promised she would be secure. Tears because he had to leave her for a while.

'Everything has fallen so quiet,' she said to Ahmed. 'I'm not attuned yet to the siesta time, and still remember how alive and noisy London is at this hour.'

'You speak like one who is homesick.'

'Not really.' She looked about her; the other people at the café tables had drifted away, and the sun was hot on the blue tiles of the mosque with its fretted minarets and those little latticed balconies. She and Raul had stood upon one at Benikesh, and there she had realised that he was invading her heart. Would her heart ever be free of him? She doubted it. Only once in a lifetime did a girl meet someone like Raul Cesar Bey, and only once did a girl run away from the chance of marrying such a man.

If it were right, if it were meant to be, then she would stay and hope to be of some joy to him. But she had seen that lovely Latin, and she had felt, especially when alone with him, that he was a man on a leash, held back from

164

reaching out for what he longed for.

'I'm half in love with El Amara,' she said quietly, 'but I know in my heart that I must leave. Perhaps in a way I am like Don Raul. I want all of a person's love, or none of it.'

'You have much courage for such a pretty little thing.' Ahmed spoke sincerely, without that flirting note in his voice.

'In comparison to someone like Doña Rachael I'm quite ordinary.' She smiled and touched the Romanos emerald. 'This is a Latin stone, meant for a Latin girl. Don Raul told me the legend of it, that it brings sadness if worn by the wrong person. I do prefer a blue jewel to something as splendid as this. It never looked right on me.'

'I think you are too modest.' Ahmed studied her slender young face. 'You have lovely eyes, and your skin is soft as a flower. I think Raul is not so aloof that he would not notice the charm about you. The cool-looking English charm.'

'I'm sure he has noticed,' she said drily. 'I know he finds me amusing to tease, but he teases Leila's baby in much the same way.'

'He looks upon you as only a child?'

'Yes.' She tinkled the charms on her wrist-chain, to which she had added a little golden frog, found for her by Leila in her trinket box.

'Then my cousin Raul must have his mind on other things! Though you are young and unsophisticated, you are far from being a child.' Ahmed laughed and shook his head at such a notion. 'Leila has fallen beneath your spell, and I have noticed the way the Princess looks at you. You intrigue her.'

'I know—and that is why I dare not stay very much longer at El Amara.'

'You think she is on the verge of suggesting to Raul that he give her a birthday gift she would really cherish?'

'Yes—and I've seen from his face that he's as tense as I am. This morning when I popped into the office to ask if I might wander around the market place he gave his consent

165

without a single objection. At Benikesh he was furious with me for going into the *souk* unattended. But I noticed how he looked at me today, as if I tried his nerves by being in his office at all. He spilled some ink on a ledger and I hastened out again. I think I am in his way . . . a hindrance rather than a help——'

There she broke off. 'Ahmed, perhaps we should go home now?'

He agreed, and while paying the waiter he asked for a *fiacre* so they wouldn't have to walk up the hill in the afternoon heat. A *fiacre* was found, and after some grumbling because they disturbed his siesta the driver agreed to drive them home. It was pleasant, the hoof beats of the horse in the quiet wending a slow way up the incline to the House of the Pomegranate.

The palm trees stood as if entranced, and the houses looked even more enclosed, with bougainvillea splashing its bright weaving of petals over the white walls that concealed the family courtyards. Ibises snoozed on their ragged nests, and the sky was hotly blue, so that when they jogged along the rim of the groves it was restful to gaze upon so much greenery. Bunches of fruits could be seen ripening on the branches, and now and then a bird hopped and pecked at something sweet.

It was amazing that here in the desert this great oasis flourished . . . a garden of Eden had been Raul's name for it. He loved and cherished every fertile tree, every acre won from the desert, and she felt hurt again by that look of his this morning . . . as if she disturbed his work and his presence of mind.

Hurt, and a little angry, she had wanted to cry out: 'You asked me to come to El Amara. You insisted. You almost abducted me . . . now you seem impatient to be rid of me. You should have known from the start that the trap I was meant to spring could trap us together, the girl from an orphanage with the grandson of a Princess. Why couldn't I see the danger? Why did you ignore it? Love isn't something to play about with. My love for you . . . yours for Rachael . . . and that of the Princess for El Amara.'

Janna shielded the tears in her eyes beneath the brim of her hat. If Ahmed noticed she could always blame them on the dazzle of the sun as they drove into the forecourt of the house. The door of the inner courtyard was flung open and there was a clatter of hooves on the tiles. As the *fiacre* came to a halt, a red-brown horse came prancing out into the sunlight, jingling his harness and tossing his mane. In the saddle sat Raul, and as Ahmed assisted Janna from the *fiacre*, he passed them with a few rapid words in Arabic. Janna caught the flash of his eyes, then the breadth of his shoulders as he galloped away.

'There has been an accident down in the groves,' said Ahmed. 'Raul is off to attend to the victim. Were you aware that he took training as a doctor?'

'Yes, he told me.'

'He is a surprising man, eh? He looks as if nature intended him to love women, but he prefers his work, and wants only one woman in his life.'

Janna nodded and walked away into the coolness of the cloisters. Here she paused and remembered how Raul had tossed her over his shoulder as if she were no more than a child to tease.

CHAPTER TWELVE

JANNA went to her room to change into something loose and cool, and she was wandering restlessly about her patio when the girl Farima came to tell her that the Princess wished to speak with her.

'Oh, but I'm so untidy—my hair!' Janna hastened to the dressing-table, picked up a comb, and dropped it nervously.

'Please?' Farima smiled and indicated that Janna sit down

on the stool while Farima tidied her hair. She took up the comb and put into Janna's hand the silver mirror whose handle was a naked goddess. Janna submitted to the girl's gentle touch, and when she looked in the mirror she found that her hair was silky and groomed, and that a light application of cream and powder concealed the marks of tears beneath her eyes.

She smiled her gratitude and Farima looked pleased and fetched from the carved cupboard a frock of softly flowered material and a pair of slippers with slightly tilted toes. Janna allowed herself to be dressed, and she had to admit that it was rather nice to be waited upon by this young girl who was so gentle and soothing. No wonder the men of the East had their *harems*. Their girls had a gift for creating harmony and relaxation, and Janna needed to feel in a calm mood. This was the first time the Princess had summoned her, and she knew that certain questions would be asked, which she must answer with a cool head.

She touched a hand to her throat and felt the beat of her pulse. The emerald gleamed against her pale skin, and her eyes looked huge and worried. Whatever would she do and say if the Princess asked outright if she loved Raul? She was not a very good actress, and she knew that it was harder to hide a secret from another woman than from a man. The Princess Yamila was shrewd; she would know instinctively that a girl as alone in the world as Janna would be almost certain to fall in love with so attractive a man, whose protective qualities were Latin, whose arrogance was often assumed like armour to guard his feelings.

Farima touched her arm, and Janna forced a smile and they left her room together and made their way to the apartment of the Princess. Their *babouches* made a whispering sound on the tiled floor, for indoors shoes were always discarded in favour of the dove-soft Eastern slippers. The sun through the scrolled ironwork of the window arches made lacy patterns, and they passed a fountain smothered in gold cassia.

At last they paused outside a doorway with a Koranic inscription carved above it in deep black letters. The door stood open, an indication that the Princess was waiting to receive her guest. Janna entered the room as nervously as a kitten, and found beneath her feet the deep softness of an Eastern carpet. To her nostrils there stole the scents of orange-flower and rosewater; overhead there was the purr of a ceiling fan, its revolving shadow on the ivory walls, a cool breath of air in this *salon* that was richly furnished with divans, little pearl-inlaid tables, screens of cedarwood, lamps of intricate design, and painted miniatures of hunters in the desert, and lovers beside lotus pools.

This room was as exotic as the Princess, who wore a *baracan* of soft lotus-gold silk. Heavy silver earrings intensified her look of fragility, but from her Raul had inherited his fine eyes; so alive, so very dark, and with a gleam of hidden fires.

The Princess held out a hand, the flash of her rings as imperious as the demand that Janna sit down beside her. Janna obeyed, and found herself at the mercy of those dark eyes so like Raul's, searching her out, taking keen notice of her fair hair, her tense young face, her hands clasped nervously in her lap.

'You are not afraid of me, I hope?' That deep voice came always as a surprise from a woman so frail.

'I am nervous, Princess,' Janna had to admit. 'Don Raul has told you about me, so you know that all this, being a guest here, meeting you, has me at a disadvantage. I am not sure how to behave.'

'You are behaving very well, my child—except in one respect, and I wish to discuss that with you. But first you must have some refreshment. Would you like a glass of mint tea, or a glass of lemonade? Perhaps even some almond milk?'

'Lemonade, please.'

The Princess smiled, as if expecting this request, and clapped her hands. Farima appeared almost at once, carrying a tray of carved copper, which was made to fit over the top of the table that stood in front of the divan. On the tray stood a carafe of lemonade with a filter of ice, slender glasses in silver holders, and a silver jug of what looked like cream.

This was almond milk, which Farima poured into a glass and handed to the Princess. She then poured cool lemonade for Janna, and withdrew as quietly as she had entered, a slim figure in silken trousers, who had looked at her mistress with devoted eyes, and who gave a clue to the kindly nature lurking beneath the autocracy and the command. The Princess was not so alarming . . . it was of falling a victim to her charm that alarmed Janna. She must be on her guard, or she would find herself admitting her love for Raul and the Princess might think this a sufficient reason for him to marry her. As a Moroccan woman she no doubt believed that it was the wife's place to love and submit, and that if Raul had these he would be content.

'You must please me and try a cake, Janna. These we call gazelle horns; they are a horn of flaky pastry filled with cream and nuts, and are quite delicious. Raul himself has a fondness for sweet things.'

A tiny flush stole into Janna's cheeks as she took a cake and held it on a serviette so the flaky crumbs wouldn't fall to the carpet. It was a pleasure to eat, and she wondered what would be the reaction of Mildred Noyes if confronted by her ex-typist taking refreshment with a real Princess. She smiled, and felt the dark eyes of Princess Yamila taking notice of her smile. Was she thinking that it was like the purr of a stray kitten given a saucer of cream?

'Raul tells me you are entirely alone in the world. It must be lonely for you, child, to have no one who is close to you. It has made you a little shy of human contacts, eh?'

'I—I suppose it has that effect, Princess, of making one either greedy for friendship, or shy of it.'

'You are a little afraid, eh? Of finding that friends can hurt you because you care for them? You want to creep into

170

a shell, like a small urchin of the sands, and hide from the hunter in a man . . . the lover?'

'I know that life has to be faced up to——'

'Life, yes. We are talking of love—do you find my grandson a handsome man?'

'I think both your grandsons are very attractive.'

'You admire Ahmed?'

'He's very easy to get along with.'

'Easier of temperament than Raul, do you find?'

'Yes, in some ways.'

'And in what way is Raul so hard that when you are in his company you look as if you would like to run and hide from him? He told me Joyosa ran away. What nonsense! Even as a schoolgirl she could never take her eyes from him, and because she was lively and pretty I hoped they might fall in love and marry when she grew into a woman. But Raul is his own man. He will bow to some of my wishes, but not all.'

The Princess fingered a bracelet on her wrist, of filigree silver and Arabian as her surroundings, and her deepest instincts. 'Please tell me why you are cool towards Raul.'

'It's just my way——' Janna's voice shook, for the conversation was getting dangerous.

'It is not our way, child. We regard warm feelings as we regard the sun; everything is enriched by its glow, and we shiver when the sun clouds over. Do you shrink from a masterful man? Do you want a tame rabbit, who will never lose his temper with you . . . or love you until the world spins over?'

The Princess smiled quizzically at Janna, and then glanced at the bracelet she wore. 'This was the betrothal gift from the man who became my husband. Raul is like him . . . do you know what the creed of the Spaniard is? That he should die a lover, and love as if each day lasted a year. Spaniards are virile men, Janna. Men of temper, passion, and vision. Men who can bear great suffering, yet who can cry like boys on the breast of a woman who gives them great happiness. They are not easy to know, or understand, but if you win the deep love of one of them, then you are rewarded beyond other women.'

Janna sat quietly intent beside the Princess, absorbed in all she had to say about life and love, and Raul in particular. She longed to know about his boyhood antics and his youthful escapades. She wanted to speak as a girl in love, but for his sake, and Rachael's, she must remain the young stranger who came to call, and left again. Raul must marry the woman of his choice. For his own sake, and for the people of El Amara, who as desert people were going to need in the future a strong leader who could safeguard their peace and security.

'I can understand your wish, Princess, to see Don Raul happily married, but I don't think he brought me here to be his—bride.'

'Why did he bring you, child?' The Princess smiled shrewdly. 'As a diversion for his persistent grandmother? Someone to amuse me in place of my ward . . . whom he meant never to marry?'

'You knew, Princess?'

'I know my grandson.'

'Then why did you send him to France to fetch her?'

'I thought he might bring Rachael Corleza instead.'

'Then you know how he feels about Doña Rachael?'

The Princess didn't answer for a moment, she just looked at Janna, slim and fair against the cushions of the divan, the great emerald weighing on her hand, a tip-tilted slipper half fallen from her left foot. 'How does he feel about Rachael, my child?'

'He—loves her.'

'You are certain of this?'

'She's very lovely—I saw them together and she wept because he had to leave her for a while. Princess, why have you never told him that you know his feelings with regard to Rachael? It would have saved him so much heart-searching.'

172

'You speak as if you want his happiness to be with a woman other than yourself.'

'I am only a friend of his.'

'And he told you Rachael was more to him than a friend?'

'He was so anxious about Rachael's security that I guessed how he felt. Love is wanting to make someone secure and happy.'

'Love is a passion, my young English girl. Love is a drive and a need. Love at times is more cruel than kind. Love is obstinate, and confusing, and a pleasure close to pain. Are you unaware of all this?'

'No——'

'Then tell me something, my child. I promise not to divulge your answer to Raul . . . do you love him?'

'Please——'

'You feel nothing for a man so tall and strong, with eyes so fine and flashing? You feel no stirring of your pulses when he looks at you?'

'It's possible to be stirred without loving someone, Princess.'

'Very true, but the hot blood of the south does not run in your veins, Janna. You have to feel love, or you feel only retreat when you are embraced. You are the cool, reserved one . . . only the right man will stir your senses.'

'It would be foolish of me to—to fall in love with Don Raul.'

'You think we can stop ourselves from falling?'

'We can fight an attraction.'

'Were you fighting it the first time I saw you with Raul?' The Princess smiled. 'I like you, Janna. You have the courage of your kind, and the cool beauty of your country.'

'I'm not beautiful,' Janna protested. 'You are kind to say so, but compared to Doña Rachael——'

'I am not comparing you to other women, my child. Rachael is a Latin, and you and she are as different as a camellia and a lily. Both in their own way are beautiful— ah, you look at me with large and wondering blue eyes. You

173

are too modest, *pequeña*. And I am sure Raul has found attractive your cool fairness and your shyness.'

'I might have teased his curiosity,' Janna admitted, 'but desire comes easy to a man, and it soon flickers out if love doesn't light the flame.'

'You are wise to know that, Janna.'

'I—I don't want to be a substitute for the woman he really loves, Princess.'

'You will never be that.' The ringed hands took Janna's and pressed them soothingly. 'I make you this promise, child, you will never be less to anyone when you deserve to be everything. You have the capacity to give much love, and it must not be given if it cannot be returned in full measure. My dear, just regard yourself as a very welcome guest in my house. Enjoy your visit, and rest assured that Raul will learn very soon that I know his secret, and that he has my consent to marry the woman of his choice.'

'He will be so happy, Princess.' Janna smiled though it hurt. She could so easily have said to the Princess, 'I want to marry your grandson,' and the impossible dream of every Cinderella would have come true for her. But it would have been a dream as fragile as the glass slipper itself, and too soon would it have broken into pieces. She loved Raul Cesar Bey, but he felt no more than a passing desire for her . . . who was not really beautiful, only fair and different to the eyes of the people here at El Amara.

With affection and homage she bent her fair head and kissed the hands of his grandmother.

'My child——'

'I shall always remember my visit to the House of the Pomegranate, Princess. Nothing like it has ever happened to me before. You have all been so kind to me.'

'There has not been too much kindness in your life, eh?'

'Only the charity kind.'

'I am happy Raul brought you here. The young devil could not have pleased me more.'

Janna gave a husky laugh. 'He can be a devil, but I

174

learned during our trip across the desert that he can also be nice. He takes after you, Princess.'

'I have always liked to think so. From a boy he has been in my keeping, and I have watched him grow into the man El Amara must have in control if the province is to survive in peace and a certain independence. The world is not the ideal place we would like it to be, Janna. There is unrest, a lack of fellowship, and one cannot be sure of abiding peace. But Raul will do his utmost for my people, and his voice will be listened to by others in authority. I am certain in my heart that he will help maintain peace in this part of the desert. I pray for it, child. With all my heart, which grows tired and is no longer the strong heart it was.'

Janna took note of the drawn look that had come over the lined but still lovely face of this woman who had governed El Amara for many years, and was now ready to let her grandson Raul take charge. Janna rose quietly to her feet and said smilingly that she would now leave the Princess to rest.

'You have a birthday to celebrate in two days' time, Princess.'

'And you think I need to ration my strength, eh?' The Princess smiled nostalgically. 'Once I could talk all night, flirt outrageously with a dozen men, and outride my own sons. Ah, it has been a good life and a long one, taking the bitter with the sweet, the sad with the beautiful. I hope you may be as happy, Janna.'

'Thank you.' Janna's smile was an aching thing on her lips, and as she left the room with its oriental furnishings and its faint aroma of incense, Farima entered to attend to her mistress. Her large brown eyes smiled into Janna's. She was a girl born and bred here at El Amara, the gentle proof of how content were the people of this desert province, and how vulnerable they would be if left to fend for themselves.

She felt both glad, and sorry, that her talk with the Princess was over, and that they had been frank with each other. So all along that shrewd old lady had known how

175

Raul felt about the lovely young widow, but she had hoped it was a mere infatuation and that he might love someone who had not already been married. But love was not so easy to manage once it took a hold on your heart; you couldn't forget it was there; you couldn't walk away from your own self.

Janna would run . . . she would depart with Ahmed without risking a goodbye to Raul. She would flee while the party was in full swing, and the Princess would understand, and Raul would soon forget that for a while a little ice-flake of an English girl had teased his curiosity.

Sunlight struck and she found herself in one of the courtyards of the house. From the look of some old and twisted myrtles she was in an unused courtyard, where the circular lily pool was clumped with flowers, and purple oleanders grew wild and tall. A cloak of rusty honeysuckle lay over a wall and within its mesh there cheeped a lonely bird. A bush of pomegranate had gone to seed and scarlet petals fell upon the old stone flags. The scent of eucalyptus hung upon the air, mingling with that of sun-warmed aged stone archways.

The place suited Janna's mood. She felt already that approach of melancholy that comes before a parting with someone beloved.

She sat down upon the stone rim of the pool and touched a floating flower. It drifted away from her fingertips and she sighed. Why did love have to hurt so much? Why couldn't a girl be gay and carefree about it, and sure of finding the same feelings with someone else? Why was she so certain that Raul would be her only love?

She rose and paced about the courtyard, and slowly the sun turned to a burning bronze in the sky and around it spread the exotic colours of an Eastern sunset.

Her gaze dwelt sad and tenderly upon the scene. To-morrow, and then again tomorrow, she would see this, the tall palm trees etched against the silk of the sky, while the hunting hawks winged dark and blinded in the glow. She would hear the song of the blackbird—the garden slave—

and the crying of quails as dusk fell over the desert and the Arabian stars began to burn in the deep violet sky.

She felt unbearably moved, and was about to go indoors when she heard the chink of a spur and saw a tall figure emerge from the shadow of an archway. Her heartbeats quickened, for no one else was quite like Raul; she would know his supple figure anywhere, the wide shoulders covered by a riding cloak whose folds fell to the glint of steel at his booted heels. He came to her, and his fingers were unclasping the cloak, and she stood very still, like a creature hunted who hoped the hunter would be kind, and let him wrap the cloak around her. His fingertips brushed her bare arms and she almost cried out, for she felt his touch to the ends of her nerves. He gazed down at her, while a breeze whispered through the palm fronds, and the spider lilies stirred at the edge of the pool.

'All alone and a little moody, eh, Janna? Do I have a place in your thoughts?'

'I was looking at the sunset. It always moves me, so splendid and then all at once the sky is dark.'

'The stars are coming out, and there is a little silver fish of a moon. Look, *chica*, have you made a wish?'

She followed his gaze to the slip of silver that had curved into view between the arching fronds of a palm tree. It shone as bright and lovely as a child's eyes, and Janna felt a single wish tearing its way to her lips. She wanted to cry out to the new moon to give her Raul's love and she would never need to wish again for anything. But she could only force a smile, pretend it was a game, and play it gamely.

'Yes, I've made a wish,' she said. 'Have you, Raul?'

'You don't often speak my name without the Spanish prefix,' he murmured. 'Are we better friends than we used to be?'

She winced at the question, for to be his friend was to be one of a crowd, even his *slougui*, the lean desert dog with its arching tail and the speed of a hare. From a rooftop the other morning, early, she had watched him race his stallion against the dog, the cloak she now wore billowing from his shoulders, which she longed to touch with her hands, feeling the hard bone and sinew of him, until he was as eager to crush as she was to be crushed.

Oh, heaven, where was the shy, alarmed typist she had been? Knowing less than a babe ... unaware, and untouched!

'I would not have seen El Amara but for you,' she said. 'I told your grandmother this afternoon that I liked being here. It's like a dream. Even when I smell the flowers, hear the cicadas and the rustling leaves, I still feel half enchanted.'

'So you have talked with Madrecita?' He seemed to speak sternly, as if he dared her to say that in some way she had spoiled his chance of having Rachael. 'Did you have an interesting talk? And may I know whether my name was mentioned?'

'It was inevitable that the Princess mention you, Don Raul.' Janna turned her eyes to his face, and the faint moonlight showed her that he looked as stern as his voice. 'I—I had to be frank with her. For both our sakes I had to tell her that you didn't bring me to El Amara with the intention of marrying me. And it's all right! She understood ... how you felt ... how we both felt about a marriage made without the proper feeling, built on a foundation not of love but of duty. She was so kind to me. She said I was to enjoy my visit here and not to be afraid that she would expect you to marry me.'

'You have been so afraid of that?' His voice held a taunting note. 'I told you myself that you were never in danger of being forced into such a predicament.'

'But you love the Princess ... you are concerned for her health, and I was afraid you might give in to her.'

'And take for myself an ice-flake for a bride?' His voice mocked, but suddenly his hands were gripping her waist beneath the folds of the cloak. At once she was on the defensive, steeling herself against a response to his touch.

She tried to pull away from him, and angrily his arms swept right around her.

'You are in no danger of becoming my reluctant bride,' he drawled, 'so we might as well enjoy the moon in the traditional manner. A moon, a garden, a girl with mysterious eyes. What more could a man ask? A man who is free of the obligation to promise his love in return for a kiss.'

'Raul ... please.'

'Well, is it not so, *niña*? You have released me from the obligation to marry you, so let us be adult and enjoy the moment. I have kissed you before ... did I not say that I might kiss you again?'

'You are being unfair ... treating me as if you want to punish me. Your grandmother had already guessed how we both felt ... nothing I said came as a real surprise to her. She is frail, but too sensible to want you to make a mess of your life by marrying the wrong person. She even knew how you felt about Joyosa, and I can't believe that you were entirely unaware of this. The pair of you have been playing a kind of game, and I wasn't going to be a pawn in it ... *Raul*, you're hurting me!'

His arms felt like steel, but it wasn't the pain of his embrace that she fought against, it was the pleasure. The longing to give in and let him punish her with kisses ... even if they were the kisses of a man aroused by anger rather than love.

'I would like to break you in half.' His voice grated low against her earlobe. 'How dare you presume to discuss my feelings with Madrecita. What do you know about the feelings of a man ... a mere slip of a girl who has never been shaken to the bone by a passion for someone, and forced to subdue it, hide it, because the time was not right for a revelation? What do you know about me, beyond what you see with your innocent blue eyes? A Spaniard with a dash of the desert in him. A man trained to demand, and yet who must give much of himself to several thousand people. A man who makes you shake at the knees, eh?'

He pulled her close and hard against him, and her knees wouldn't have supported her if he had let her go instead. His dark head came down to hers, his eyes searched her face, and a smile twisted the edge of his lip. 'You may well look afraid,' he taunted. 'This courtyard is in the old part of the house, and there is no one to see us, no other soul but the owl that has flown about here since I was a boy.'

'You are being a devil,' she gasped, twisting her face away from his mocking, searching lips, and giving a little cry as their warmth pressed into the hollow of her throat. He laughed against her lips and silenced them, and she felt helpless, as if flames crept near and she must run yet was unable to move.

Then she seemed to be floating, even as he kissed her, and realised that he was carrying her into the shadows of an archway. A mass of honeysuckle grew there, falling to the ground to form a carpet of rusty-gold petals and a dizzying scent. She felt them beneath her, crushed by her slight weight as she was crushed by the lean strength of Raul. He held her there, slender and pale on the dark cloak and the honeysuckle, and she beat with her hands at his face, his shoulders, his laughing mouth.

'You little fool, Janna. Your blows don't hurt me, and you have not the spite to claw at my eyes.'

'I hate you ... hate you ...'

'That is understood,' he mocked, and with a deliberate movement of his hand he bared her shoulder and kissed her soft white skin. 'This is what you have feared all along, eh? The little English girl forced to submit to the embraces of a desert man. Forced to give her lips to his kisses. Poor Janna! If I had known your terror was this great, then I should have left you to the tender mercy of Madam Noyes. I am sure she would have taken you back as her little runabout ... after all, it isn't every girl who wishes to make a vocation of spinsterhood.'

'I—I'd sooner be a spinster than just an object!'

'My dear girl, you are rather more decorative than a mere object.'

'Y-you know what I mean.'

'*Niña*, I am in no mood for solving puzzles.' His lips travelled the line of her cheek to her earlobe, and at their touch she grew desperate.

'It amuses you to play about with me ... because I'm shy, and I have no money, a-and no one of my own to turn to. You get a kick out of using your charm on me ... because you're rich and privileged, a-and attractive!'

'I am the complete rake, eh?'

'Right now you're behaving like one!'

'You dislike my kisses that much?'

'I find them hateful.' And it was true; these were not kisses of love and so they were unbearable to her. They made her feel ashamed, because she wanted to respond to them. They made her ache to her heart—and suddenly she began to cry. The stormy tears filled her eyes and ran down her cheeks, and she was hurt and tormented, by Raul, by the moon and the honeysuckle, and the startled hoot of the little owl who usually had this place to himself.

She put her hands over her face and cried as if she were a child again, shut alone in the dormitory, punished for diving into the icy stream because she saw someone in trouble and wanted to help. She had been chastised, told off for going into the stream when she couldn't swim.

Tonight Raul was angry with her. She had risked upsetting his beloved Princess, and though she could understand his concern, she didn't know why he had to be cruel with her. It was cruel of him to kiss her when he didn't care, and to threaten even more when he held her, crying and captive, on the crushed flowers.

'Janna, what a child you really are.' He pulled her hands from her wet eyes and began to mop up her tears with a large handkerchief. 'I forget that you are different in ways from the girls of El Amara. Your upbringing has made you extra-sensitive, and unsure.'

181

'I expect you mean naïve, *señor*, but I have my pride.'

'Yes, you have your pride, *chica*. Now have the tears decided to leave off?'

'Yes, thank you.'

'Come, then.' He lifted her to her feet and brushed the honeysuckle petals from the cloak he drew around her. Her hair was a pale, silky ruffle framing her tear-stained face. 'You do look forlorn, Janna, as if I had done something terrible to you. You make me feel I have hurt you ... are you bruised?'

'No——' But she was bruised at heart, and she felt almost as cold as when the angry teacher had pulled her out of the stream and given her a push towards the tall grey building that had been her only home.

Two large tears spilled again from her eyes, and she turned away from Raul so he wouldn't see them.

'Let us go in.' He spoke with a sudden chilly note in his voice. 'It will be almost time for dinner.'

'May I be excused?' Her voice held a tremor.

'You are afraid the family will notice that you have been crying?'

'Yes—it would be embarrassing.'

'But Leila sometimes weeps, when Kassim is a little cruel to her. Men are not angels, *chica*.'

'Leila loves her husband ... I daresay she understands him, and forgives.'

'Love is like that, ch?'

'I should imagine so.'

'But I must remain unforgiven?'

'For tonight,' Janna admitted, upset, torn by mixed emotions, needing to be alone. 'Will you allow me to stay in my room? I have no appetite for dinner, and no heart for pretending to be gay when I feel the opposite.'

'Janna——'

'Please be kind to me ... if you can be without having to make the effort.' Then in a torment that had to find expression in action, she tore off his hindering cloak, dropped

182

it to the ground, and fled into the house away from him. One of her *babouches* came off and she left it behind her, feeling the coldness of the tiles beneath her bare foot. She came to the corridor that led to her apartment, and gave a little cry as she ran full tilt into a silent-footed servant. She was aware of the man's startled gaze as she ran on until she came to the entrance of her rooms. It was a relief to close the door behind her and to sink down on a divan with her chaotic thoughts.

She clenched a cushion with her cold hands and felt the pressure of Raul's emerald against her fine-boned finger. She needed no reminder of his kisses, their touch still lingered on her lips, her neck, her eyes.

She must get away! She couldn't face seeing him again .. yet she had to in the morning.

With a troubled sigh she rose to her feet and entered the room with the sunken marble bath. She would bathe her aches away, and then go to bed.

'Have I hurt you?' He had asked her that, and she gazed with shocked eyes at the bruise that came to light on her arm when she peeled off her clothes and let them fall to the coloured tiles. She touched with her fingertips the petal-shaped violet mark, reminding her vividly of the crush of his arms, the dizzying scent of the honeysuckle, the twisted myrtles like wraiths in the moonlight.

She slipped into the scented steam of her bath and the warm silky water felt soothing against her skin. Pale skin, long slim legs, a slightly curved bosom that guarded her heart and its secret.

Suddenly she heard footsteps, but was not disturbed. It would be Farima with some food on a tray and a pot of delicious Arabian coffee. She lifted an arm above the water to wave to the girl.

'I will put the tray just here on this stool.'

She looked up wildly, and there was Raul, unperturbed to find her in the bath, standing tall beside it with the air of a man who would hold the towel for her if she wished to come out.

'I—I thought you were Farima!' she gasped.

'Do I look like her?' he drawled. 'You dropped your slipper, Cinderella. I came to return it, and to bring you some food and coffee. Unless you promise to eat something before going to bed, I shall stay to see that you do.'

'You'll go ... this instant!' Her cheeks were scarlet, and she held the sponge protectively against her. He really was a devil! Standing there, so lithe and dark, unrepentant about that interlude in the courtyard, tormenting her again with his roving, dark-lashed eyes.

'Raul ... please go.'

He smiled slowly. 'When you beg so prettily I have to stay out of the sheer inability to leave you.'

'Y-you aren't at all nice to me tonight.'

'No, because I was concerned for Madrecita. But I found her looking very pleased with herself. She enjoyed your little talk and said you were a nice girl who wanted me to be happy ... do you want that, *chica*?'

'I suppose so. What will become of El Amara if you don't get what you want? You are an arrogant man, Raul Cesar Bey, but you're the best man for the job.'

'You little fraud!'

'W-what?' Her great blue eyes met his, startled, bewildered, begging him to go, to stay, to explain himself.

'You utter child!' He laughed and it rang out resonantly in the marbled bathroom. 'Did you really get it into your funny head that I was madly in love with Rachael Corleza?'

'But you are ... in love with her.'

'Am I? Many thanks for knowing the state of my mind, and my heart, better than I know them myself.'

'The Princess knows how you feel about Rachael.'

'My grandmother has always known of my regard for my lovely cousin by marriage. Rachael made her husband a good wife, and we all hope that one day she will marry again. Someone lovely should not be alone, without a man in her life.'

'But——' Words failed Janna, and she shrank among the soap bubbles as he knelt, smiling, beside the bath and gazed down at her, a look in his eyes that made her desperately aware of her almost transparent cloak of scented foam.

'I—I want to come out, Raul. Won't you go into the other room . . . we can talk there.'

'Of course, little one.' He leapt to his feet and carried her supper tray into the adjoining *salon*. On trembling legs she climbed from the bath and quickly dried herself. She slipped into a silk wrap, and found that he had placed her lost *babouche* beside its mate. She put them on, and it took all her courage to join him. He lounged on the divan, where she had sat an hour ago, and he was pouring coffee into a pair of cups with bluebirds painted on them.

'Come.' His eyes drew her towards him. 'A cup of coffee will steady your shaken nerves.'

'Raul . . .' Her knees were weak as she sank down on a huge velvet cushion, a slender figure in lemon silk, beseeching eyes raised to him. 'What has your grandmother told you . . . about me?'

'It was a little wicked of her to give you away, eh?'

'Oh, this is so embarrassing.'

'Your coffee, *niña*, just as you like it.'

'Thank you.' She took several heartening sips of the delicious brew. 'You surely don't believe what your grandmother told you.'

'Don't you want me to believe her, Janna?'

'It might be better if you didn't.'

'I think it would be infinitely desirable if I did.'

'Really?' Her eyes widened and were held by his. She was at his knees on the velvet cushion, her hair in damp tendrils at her temples and the nape of her neck, a slim young slave of feelings she could barely fight any more.

'Don't you wish to know why I want to believe what the Princess confided to me?'

'She promised not to tell you.'

'I confess that I coaxed your secret out of her . . . not that she took much coaxing.'

'And I suppose you want to hear me say it, so you can laugh!' She was poised to feel from him again when he swiftly caught her hands in his and held her captive.

'Don't speak to me like that, Janna, or I shall become as dangerous as you have always thought me.' Raul drew her firmly, gently, inescapably into his arms, and his hand stroked her soft hair, her thin cheek, the curve of her shoulder. 'Why be afraid of me, *niña*? I only love you.'

'Raul——'

'I loved you from the moment you looked at me with those big blue eyes that hungered for affection. Little waif. Little runabout. Fighting me every inch of the way from the beach to Benikesh, from the mosque balcony to the old courtyard tonight. Why, in heaven's name?'

'Because I thought you loved Rachael.'

'Did I not warn you not to let your imagination run away with you?' He gave her a tiny shake, and then he gathered her closer still to the warm muscles beneath the silky white shirt. Warm-skinned, tawny, tormenting man. With an incoherent little murmur she buried her face against him.

'Y-you didn't kiss me, Raul, like a man who cared. You were being cruel.'

'And you were being cool . . . too cool for my desert liking.' He tilted her chin, made her look at him as he read deeply of her eyes. 'So I was all set to be the bridegroom of Rachael, who would be most alarmed if she knew. She finds me a terrible tyrant. Her husband was much more like Ahmed.'

Janna gave a start at his mention of Ahmed, who had been so sure that she was not the girl for Raul. Was he right? Should she still run away as planned?

'Raul, would it work out . . . you and I?'

'Like honey and toast, *mi querida*,' he grinned, and dropped a kiss on her nose. 'Like snow and flame.'

'Meaning I must melt for you?'

'Mmmm.' He lowered his head and kissed her lips very

186

slowly, lingering on their shy softness, caressing, possessing, but no longer hurting her in anger. 'Melt and be sweet, my Janna. I want you so much. I want to love you, to make you safe, to make you know what it is to be part of someone. I want the Princess to announce our coming marriage the evening of her birthday. It will be the best gift we could give her.'

Janna took a deep breath, unbelieving and yet beginning to believe in the warm and wonderful reality of Raul's love. It was there in his eyes, in his touch, in the firm and tender clasp of his arms. It was for her, if she had the courage to take it. The love of Raul Cesar Bey, who would be the next governor of El Amara, with whom she would live on the edge of the tawny sands, in the House of the Pomegranate.

'Then let us give the Princess her gift.' Janna spoke shyly. 'I should like to marry you, if you really want me.'

'Shall I demonstrate how much, Janna?' His eyes smiled down into hers, a gleam of devilment in them. 'Can you take it, or do you need some food to strengthen you?'

'What did you bring me?'

'All the things you like best . . . including myself.'

'Arrogant man!'

'But you love me for it.'

'More than you deserve.' Her arms crept around his bronzed neck. 'It was never true, Raul, that I was afraid of your desire. I was only afraid of loving you too much, and not being loved in return. I so believed my own fiction about you and Rachael. I wonder why?'

'I imagine it was a defence action against me.' He smiled and cradled her close to him. 'An instinctive retreat into fantasy because you were a little afraid of the sheik in me.'

She touched his brown throat with a shy hand, and the emerald glowed as he took her hand and pressed a kiss deep into her palm.

'Do you see, *querida*, the stone has come truly alive and I think at last that the temple dancer of long ago would be happy for us. You are all that a man could desire, kind and

187

impulsive of heart, innocent and quietly ardent, and lovely for me.'

Smiling into her eyes, he kissed the ring and so he pledged that soon they would be married, and her heart told her that she need have no more doubts about their future together. He had conquered her and all her fears, and she recalled little things he had said to her in the desert, which in her innocence she had not fully understood. Even then he had been saying he loved her.

'Raul, I'm so very happy,' she whispered, and with a blissful smile she gave herself to his kiss, a slight young thing in silk, lost in the arms of her desert lover.

FREE!
Harlequin Romance Catalogue

Here is a wonderful opportunity to read many of the Harlequin Romances you may have missed.

The HARLEQUIN ROMANCE CATALOGUE lists hundreds of titles which possibly are no longer available at your local bookseller. To receive your copy, just fill out the coupon below, mail it to us, and we'll rush your catalogue to you!

Following this page you'll find a sampling of a few of the Harlequin Romances listed in the catalogue. Should you wish to order any of these immediately, kindly check the titles desired and mail with coupon.

Have You Missed Any of These
Harlequin Romances?

- [ ] 825 MAKE UP YOUR MIND, NURSE
  Phyllis Matthewman
- [ ] 841 DOCTOR IN BRAZIL
  Patricia Fenwick
- [ ] 844 NURSE ALISON'S TRUST
  Mary Burchell
- [ ] 850 NURSE ANNE'S IMPERSON-
  ATION   Caroline Trench
- [ ] 856 TOO YOUNG TO MARRY
  Rosalind Brett
- [ ] 858 MY SURGEON NEIGHBOUR
  Jane Arbor
- [ ] 861 BEWILDERED HEART
  Kathryn Blair
- [ ] 866 DOCTOR LUKE   Lilian Chisholm
- [ ] 872 HAVEN OF THE HEART
  Averil Ives
- [ ] 873 NURSE JULIE OF WARD
  THREE   Joan Callender
- [ ] 878 THIS KIND OF LOVE
  Kathryn Blair
- [ ] 892 THE LOCAL DOCTOR
  Juliet Armstrong
- [ ] 895 AND FALSELY PLEDGE MY
  LOVE   Mary Burchell
- [ ] 898 DOCTOR ROBERT COMES
  AROUND   Nan Asquith
- [ ] 900 THERE CAME A SURGEON
  Hilda Pressley
- [ ] 969 NURSE AFLOAT   Jane Marnay
- [ ] 1063 THE MAN FROM RHODESIA
  Ruth Clemence
- [ ] 1064 MISTRESS OF THE HOUSE
  Eleanor Farnes
- [ ] 1065 STUDENT NURSE AT SWALE
  Pauline Ash
- [ ] 1066 NURSE AT STE. MONIQUE
  Juliet Armstrong
- [ ] 1067 TERRACE IN THE SUN
  Anne Weale
- [ ] 1068 THE DUTCH UNCLE
  Margery Hilton
- [ ] 1969 THE MAN FROM THE VALLEY
  Joyce Dingwell
- [ ] 1070 THE DRUMMER OF CORRAE
  Jean S. Macleod
- [ ] 1071 SPICED WITH CLOVES
  Elizabeth Hunter

- [ ] 1072 THE YOUNG AMANDA
  Sara Seale
- [ ] 1077 THE GOLDEN VALLEY
  Hilary Wilde
- [ ] 1645 BRIDE OF THE RIF
  Margaret Rome
- [ ] 1647 THE SWEET SPRING
  Hilda Nickson
- [ ] 1648 MOONLIGHT AND MAGIC
  Rachel Lindsay
- [ ] 1649 SWEET KATE   Lucy Gillen
- [ ] 1652 A PEARL FOR LOVE
  Mary Cummins
- [ ] 1653 THE TARTAN TOUCH
  Isobel Chace
- [ ] 1654 IN THE SHADE OF THE
  PALMS   Roumelia Lane
- [ ] 1655 IT'S RUMOURED IN THE
  VILLAGE   Mary Burchell
- [ ] 1656 AUTUMN OF THE WITCH
  Anne Mather
- [ ] 1657 WIFE TO SIM   Joyce Dingwell
- [ ] 1658 DEAR PURITAN
  Violet Winspear
- [ ] 1659 A PARADE OF PEACOCKS
  Elizabeth Ashton
- [ ] 1660 A STRANGER CAME
  Jane Donnelly
- [ ] 1661 OLIVE ISLAND   Kay Thorpe
- [ ] 1662 A SERPENT IN EDEN
  Eleanor Farnes
- [ ] 1663 THE CAVE OF THE WHITE
  ROSE   Flora Kidd
- [ ] 1666 SATURDAY'S CHILD
  Betty Neels
- [ ] 1669 A TIME REMEMBERED
  Lucy Gillen
- [ ] 1670 FRAIL SANCTUARY
  Margery Hilton
- [ ] 1671 MANDOLINS OF MONTORI
  Iris Danbury
- [ ] 1698 CADENCE OF PORTUGAL
  Isobel Chace
- [ ] 1699 SUNSHINE ON THE MOUN-
  TAINS   Margaret Malcolm
- [ ] 1700 GONE BEFORE MORNING
  Lilian Peake

All books are 60c. Please use the handy order coupon.

Have You Missed Any of These
Harlequin Romances?

All books are 60c. Please use the handy order coupon.